D1491129

ORIGIN OF THE SOLAR SYSTEM

Origin of the Solar System

Proceedings of a conference held at the Goddard Institute for Space Studies, New York - - - - January 23-24, 1962

Edited by

ROBERT JASTROW

A. G. W. CAMERON

Institute for Space Studies
Goddard Space Flight Center
National Aeronautics and Space Administration
New York, New York

1963

ACADEMIC PRESS
New York • London

ACADEMIC PRESS INC.
111 Fifth Avenue, New York 3, N. Y.

United Kingdom Edition published by
ACADEMIC PRESS INC. (LONDON) LTD.
Berkeley Square House, London W.1

LIBRARY OF CONGRESS CATALOG CARD NUMBER: 63-20027

PRINTED IN THE UNITED STATES OF AMERICA

LIST OF CONTRIBUTORS

Numbers in parentheses indicate the pages on which the author's contribution begins

E. ANDERS (95), Enrico Fermi Institute for Nuclear Studies, Departments of Chemistry and Geophysical Sciences, University of Chicago, Chicago, Illinois

A. G. W. CAMERON (4, 55, 85), Institute for Space Studies, NASA Goddard Space Flight Center, New York, New York

WILLIAM A. FOWLER (77), California Institute of Technology, Pasadena, California

THOMAS GOLD (171), Center for Radiophysics and Space Research, Cornell University, Ithaca, New York

FRED HOYLE (63), St. John's College, Cambridge, England

ROBERT JASTROW, Institute for Space Studies, NASA Goddard Space Flight Center, New York, New York

G. J. F. MACDONALD (155), Institute of Geophysics and Planetary Physics, University of California, Los Angeles, California

E. OPIK (73), Department of Physics and Astronomy, University of Maryland, College Park, Maryland

LYMAN SPITZER (39), Princeton University Observatory, Princeton, New Jersey

H. E. SUESS (143), Department of Chemistry, University of California, San Diego, La Jolla, California

D. TER HAAR (4), The Clarendon Laboratory, Oxford, England

J. A. WOOD (147), Enrico Fermi Institute for Nuclear Studies, University of Chicago, Chicago, Illinois, and Smithsonian Astrophysical Observatory, Cambridge, Massachusetts

PREFACE and INTRODUCTION

On January 23 and 24, 1962, the Institute for Space Studies was host to an international group of scientists from many fields, gathered to discuss the origin and development of the solar system. The subject of this informal conference is one of the oldest unsolved questions of natural philosophy. Relatively modern discussions date back to Descartes (1644), Kant (1755), and LaPlace (1796). The problem has continued to interest some of the keenest minds in the history of science, but relatively little progress has been made since the Eighteenth Century, owing to the scarcity of data relating to the problem. However, in recent years a great deal of relevant information has been secured from the investigation of meteorites. With the development of space exploration we shall soon be in a position to read the early history of the solar system as it is preserved in the surface features and internal structure of the moon. The quickening interest aroused by these recent investigations and the future prospects for physical exploration of the moon and planets led to the organization of this meeting on the subject.

During the long history of the speculations relating to the origin of the planets, two general schools of thought arose. One school held that a catastrophe occurred on a stellar scale in which the planets were formed as a by-product. Especially common was the notion that a near collision of two stars may have led to the ejection of a filament of gas, from which condensation into planetary bodies subsequently occurred.

Such collision or *catastrophic* theories had their progenitor in the ideas of Buffon (1745), and in more modern form were discussed by Chamberlin, Moulton, Jeans, and Jeffries. Until recently the catastrophic theories had wide acceptance. However, serious difficulties have been noted by students of the subject, among which may be mentioned the fact that the line of droplets of protoplanetary material drawn out of tidal attractions, when captured by the sun, will be in elongated orbits of large eccentricity. This prediction is in contrast to the observed nearly perfect circularity of the orbits of the planet. Furthermore, Lyttleton has shown that 99% of the mass drawn from the sun would fall back into it as the intruding star receded.

The other theory is the nebular or *condensation* hypothesis, which originated with Descartes, and after falling into disfavor, has in recent years been revived and has come to the forefront in current treatments of the problem. This hypothesis provided the basis for most of the conference discussion.

The nebular hypothesis suggests that planets were created as minor condensations in the process of gravitational contraction which led to the formation of the primitive sun out of the gas and dust of interstellar space. As the protosun contracts it must spin faster in order to conserve the angular momentum and must shed mass in an equatorial plane, thus leaving behind a nebular disk. In this theory it is presumed that the planets were formed by some further process of condensation out of the matter of the disk.

The condensation theory fits into the context of the modern ideas on stellar formation and evolution—a circumstance which contributes to the high regard in which this theory is now held. Also, it naturally predicts circularity and coplanarity of orbits. However, the course of the conference discussion indicates three primary difficulties, which have resisted a quantitative attack until now.

Foremost is the problem of the distribution of angular momentum between the sun and the planets. The primitive sun should preserve most of its angular momentum as it contracts and have a greater share of the angular momentum in the solar system. It is observed, however, that 98% of the angular momentum in the solar system resides in the planets, and only 2% in the sun. It was the failure to account for the loss of angular momentum by the contracting sun which led to the abandonment of the condensation hypothesis for 150 years.

Second, a substantial fraction of the mass of the solar nebula should be in the disk, but actually the planets have 0.1% of the mass. What happened to the missing material? Perhaps streams of energetic particles from the surface of the sun blasted it away, or it may have evaporated from the outer boundary. It is possible that both mechanisms were effective—the first removing the matter close to the sun, and the second removing it at the boundary of the solar system.

Third, it is difficult to understand the mechanism for accumulation of solid matter out of planetary debris. It is easy to think of this accumulation as occurring in a condensation of a planetary-sized body of gas, within the solar nebula, as an analogue to the initial process of condensation which formed the sun. The difficulty is that a body the size of the earth would be large enough to keep such heavy gases as xenon bound to itself during the history of its contraction. But the abundance of xenon on the earth is far lower than we would expect if this were the case.

In recent years these difficulties have loomed larger as increasingly serious efforts are made to place the nebular theory on a quantitative basis. Most of the conference discussion revolved about these three central points, and their salient features were summarized very skillfully in the concluding paper by Thomas Gold.

The other papers are included here in approximately the order of their presentation at the conference. The earlier papers are concerned with the processes of star formation and the associated phenomena that may result in the formation of a planetary system. The later papers deal with the chemical and physical properties of the meteorites and the planets and with their relation to the early history of the solar system. It is interesting to note that both of these lines of inquiry are less than a decade old.

Five formal papers and several informal ones were read during the two-day period of the meeting. The entire proceedings were recorded on tape and subsequently transcribed. These transcriptions were then edited and revised to form the basis of most of the material contained in this volume.

The editors have prefaced the papers which were presented at the conference by a historical account of the earlier developments in the field. They are grateful to Dr. D. ter Haar for allowing his unpublished discussion of this history to be adapted for the present volume. They also wish to express their appreciation to Lyons T. Carr and Nicholas Panagakos for their assistance in editing the proceedings, and to Arthur Levine and Lois Zapolsky for assisting in the organization of the meeting.

R. JASTROW

A. G. W. CAMERON

April 1963

CONTENTS

Historical Review of Theories of the Origin of the Solar System

D. TER HAAR and A. G. W. CAMERON

Star Formation

LYMAN SPITZER, JR.

Contraction of the Sun toward the Main Sequence

A. G. W. CAMERON

Formation of the Planets

FRED   HOYLE

Dissipation of the Solar Nebula

E. OPIK

Formation of Light Nuclei

WILLIAM A. FOWLER

The Formation of the Solar Nebula

A. G. W. CAMERON

Meteorites and the Early History of the Solar System

EDWARD ANDERS

Historical Review of Theories of the Origin of the Solar System

D. TER HAAR AND A. G. W. CAMERON

The Clarendon Laboratory, Oxford, England; and NASA Goddard Institute for Space Studies, New York City.

In this chapter, we shall give a historical survey of many of the theories dealing with the origin of the planetary system. No attempt is made to give a complete survey, but it is believed that the more important contributions have been discussed. Even though this problem is perhaps the oldest unsolved problem of scientific philosophy, there is a mounting interest in it, as can be judged from the fact that a majority of the theories to be discussed here have been proposed since 1938.

Most of the historical discussion of the problem of the origin of the solar system has been concerned with the explanation of only a small number of observational facts. We can summarize these facts under five headings.

(A) *Regularity of planetary orbits.* All planetary orbits are nearly circular and are nearly co-planar. The direction of motion of the planets around the sun is the same for all of them and is also the same as the direction of the rotation of the sun itself. We shall call this *direct rotation*.

(B) *Similarity between planetary systems and satellite systems.* Most satellites have orbital paths of small eccentricities; we shall call these "regular" satellites. There are a small number of "irregular" satellites that do not possess this property; we shall not discuss these here. The regular satellites have an orbital plane that is about the same as the equatorial plane of their primary, analogous to the approximate equality between the orbital planes of the planets and the equatorial plane of the sun. The orbital eccentricities of both the planets and the satellite systems are small. The total mass of the satellite systems tends to lie around 10^{-3} of the primary mass; the planets have a total mass of approximately 10^{-3} of the sun.

1

The earth–moon system is an obvious major exception to this rule. For the extensive satellite systems of the outer planets, there is an approximate exponential increase in the distances of the planets, similar to the Titius–Bode law for the planets to be discussed below. The direction of orbital movement of the satellites is in the same direction as the rotation of its primary, just as the direction of orbital motion of the planets is in the same direction as that of the solar rotation.

(*C*) *The difference between terrestrial and giant planets.* While the terrestrial planets are small, heavy, near the sun, and have a slow rotation and few satellites, the giant planets are large, light, further from the sun, and possess extensive satellite systems, and rotate relatively rapidly.

(*D*) *The Titius–Bode Law.* The mean distance of the *n*th planet from the sun is, to a good approximation, given by the law:

$$r_n = r_0 m^n \tag{1}$$

with $m = 1.89$. This expression represents the mean distances slightly better than the older Titius–Bode law:

$$r_n = a + b2^n, \tag{2}$$

and we shall in the following always represent the observational mean distances by equation (1) and still call it the Titius–Bode law. It has to be remembered that in numbering the planets, the asteroids are together counted as one planet.

(*E*) *The slow rotation of the sun.* If the sun had condensed from a gas which at any moment had moved with Keplerian velocities, its rotational velocity would be about 200 times larger than at present. Thus we would naively expect that the sun should contain much more angular momentum than the planets in the solar system. In fact, the reverse is the case. This fact has been extensively discussed in connection with the processes for the formation of the solar system.

Historically, there have been essentially two different ways of approaching the problem of the origin of the solar system. The first class of theories considers a *closed* system. This is a development of the sun and possibly a solar envelope, which starts with protosun rather than the sun itself. Belot calls these theories *monistic*. In many instances, the sun is supposed to have essentially the same physical properties that it has at present, apart, perhaps, from its angular momentum.

The second class of theories considers *open* systems. The interaction between the sun and some foreign body is supposed to have been the first step in the developments leading to our planetary system. Belot calls these theories *dualistic*. It is immediately clear that there is more freedom in dualistic theories.

The older theories have been extensively discussed in the literature [16, 18, 27, 39]. Recent theories, starting with Berlage's theories, have not yet been discussed critically and we shall, therefore, discuss these theories more extensively.

This introduction may appropriately be ended with two quotations. Though both refer more specifically to general cosmogonies, their general ideas also apply to theories about the origin of the solar system. The first is from Poincaré's monograph [10]:

"It is impossible to contemplate the spectacle of the starry universe without wondering how it was formed: perhaps we ought to wait to look for a solution until we have patiently assembled the elements, and until we have thereby acquired some hope of finding a solution; but if we were so reasonable, if we were curious without impatience, it is probable that we would never have created Science and that we would always have been content with a trivial existence. Thus the mind has imperiously laid claim to this solution long before it was ripe, even while perceived in only faint glimmers—allowing us to guess a solution rather than wait for it. It is for this reason that cosmogonic hypotheses are so numerous and varied; it is for this reason that every day new ones spring up, equally as uncertain but nevertheless as plausible as the more ancient theories. The new ones take their place among the old ones without detracting from their validity."[1]

The second quotation, from Kant's cosmogonical works, shows very well the feelings of the many scientists who have endeavored to give a theory about the origin of the solar system [3]:

"Upon a slight conjecture I have ventured on a dangerous journey and I already behold the foothills of new lands. Those who have the courage to continue the search will set foot on them."[2]

---

[1] "Il est impossible de contempler le spectacle de l'univers étoilé sans se demander comment il s'est formé: nous devions peut-être attendre pour chercher une solution que nous ayons patiemment rassemblé les éléments, et que nous ayons acquis par là quelque espoir de la trouver; mais si nous étions si raisonnables, si nous étions curieux sans impatience, il est probable que nous n'avions jamais créé la Science et que nous nous serions toujours contentés de vivre notre petite vie. Notre esprit a donc reclamé impérieusement cette solution bien avant qu'elle fut mûre, et alors qu'il ne possédait que de vagues lueurs, lui permettant de la deviner plutôt que de l'attendre. Et c'est pour cela que les hypothèses cosmogoniques sont si nombreuses, si variées, qu'il en nait chaque jour de nouvelles, tout aussi incertaines, mais tout aussi plausibles que les théories plus anciennes, au milieu desquelles elles viennent prendre place sans parvenir à les faire oublier."

[2] "Ich have auf eine geringe Vermutung eine gefährliche Reise gewagt und erblicke schon die Vorgebirge neuer Länder. Diejenigen, welche die Herzhaftigkeit haben die Untersuchung fortzusetzen, werden sie betreten."

I. Descartes' Vortex Theory [1]

Descartes, who is often called the father of modern philosophy, can also be rightly called the father modern cosmogony. As we shall see in this section, his cosmogony can no longer be accepted as the final answer to the problem. This is not strange if we remember that the general law of gravitation had not yet been found by Newton in 1644 when Descartes published his cosmogony. In considering Descartes' work, we should not so much use modern standards to judge his scientific results as to judge his scientific methods. Descartes was one of the first modern scientists trying to find laws of nature and trying to derive from these laws results that might be tested by further observation. Of course, in the 17th century, religion still reigned supreme, but Descartes made the relevant remark that even if God had created the world without much regularity, the laws of nature would select from all possible configurations those that have the greatest stability. In his commentaries on Descartes, Malebranche writes, "If God had created the sun as a cube, the laws of motion would soon have produced a spherical form."[3] This is, of course, quite a long way from the medieval idea that the sun was spherical because that was the most beautiful form.

Descartes then proceeds to show that the vortex shape of the solar system is a stationary one. He assumes that space is not empty but filled with ether (Descartes does not use the term *materia aethera* but Leibniz and Huygens did in discussing Descartes' ideas.) The only possible motion in space is then in closed orbits:

> ". . . When a body leaves its place, it always enters another body's place, and this body enters that of another, and so forth, on to the last, which occupies at the same instant the spot vacated by the first body. Now we do not generally notice these circular movements when bodies move in the air because we are accustomed to think of air only as empty

---

[3] Free translation.

[4] ". . . Quand un corps quitte sa place, il entre toujours en celle d'un autre, et celui-ci en celle d'un autre, et ainsi de suite jusqu'au dernier, qui occupe au même instant le lieu délaissé par le premier . . . Or nous ne remarquons pas communément ces mouvements circulaires quand les corps se remuent en l'air, parce que nous sommes accoutumés de ne concevoir l'air que comme un espace vide; mais voyez nager des poissons dans le bassin d'une fontaine, s'ils ne s'approchent point trop près de la surface de l'eau, ils ne la feront point du tout branler, encore qu'ils passent dessous avec une très grande vitesse; d'où il paroît manifestement que l'eau qu'ils poussent devant eux ne pousse pas indifféremment toute l'eau du bassin, mais seulement celle qui peut mieux servir à parfaire le cercle de leur mouvement, et rentrer en la place qu'ils abandonnent." (La monde ou traité de la lumière, Chapter IV. "Oeuvres de Descartes," Vol. 4, p. 232. V. Cousin, Paris, 1824.

space. But just watch fish swimming in a pond; if they do not come too close to the surface of the water, they will not make it shimmer at all, even though they pass underneath very swiftly. Thus it seems obvious that the water they push in front of them does not indiscriminately move all the water in the pond, but only that water which makes up the circle of their movement—that water which moves to fill the space they vacate."

In a universe filled with ether and matter, the only possible motion would thus be a vortex motion. As soon as motion was imparted by God to matter, vortices were set up: innumerable more or less circular eddies of all sizes. The friction between the eddies would "file" down the rough shape of the primordial matter. The filings tend towards the centre of the vortex, forming the sun. The finer larger pieces of matter tend to fly out of the vortex forming the transparent heavens, while the coarser bodies are captured in the vortex; this third kind of matter forms the earth and the other planets. Around these planets, secondary vortices are formed, in which the satellites are captured. This picture is remarkably similar to the cosmogonical ideas of von Weizsäcker, which will be discussed later.

There are, of course, many objections that can be raised against the vortex theory in its original form. First of all, the analogy between the plane of the ecliptic and the surface of a whirling waterpool is completely fortuitous. The vortices should have been pictured three-dimensionally and no plane would then be present. We may also mention Newton's criticism. Newton pointed out that one would not be able to obtain Kepler's third law, relating the period of a planet with its distance from the sun, from any detailed theory of vortex motion.

It is of interest to note here how Descartes' theory was an attempt to reconcile the Copernican ideas about the earth rotating around the sun (as is the case in the large vortex) with the earth at the center of the universe (which it is in its own secondary vortex). In 1633, Descartes had heard about Galileo's fate, and, therefore, he did not finish a book entitled *The World*, in which the Copernican hypothesis was adopted. Instead he developed the vortex theory, which was much more orthodox.

Newton was far more orthodox in his attitude towards the origin of the solar system, preferring a creation by God to a physical development. Laplace wrote about this attitude:

"I cannot but note how much Newton departs here from the method which he applied so successfully elsewhere."[5]

---

[5] "Je ne puis m'empêcher d'observer combien Newton s'est écarté sur ce point de la méthode dont il a fait ailleurs de si heureuses applications."

The real development of this branch of cosmogony only started after the French Revolution had uprooted the theological influence on science, although the 18th century has produced the theories of Buffon and Kant, which are the forerunners of practically all modern theories, with very few exceptions.

II. The First Tidal Theory [2]

In 1745, Buffon suggested that a comet hitting the sun might have been responsible for tearing from the sun sufficient material to produce planets. Since the sun might have been hit skewly by the comet, the rotation of the planets can be understood. Buffon suggests that the planetary rotation was sufficiently fast to cause rotational instability, thus producing the satellite systems. The collision could also have produced the solar rotation.

It must be remarked here that in Buffon's time fantastic ideas about comets were common. Buffon estimated the mass of the comet of 1680 as 28,000 times the earth's mass, that is, about one solar mass. It is, therefore, clear that Buffon really had in mind encounters like the one considered in the modern tidal theories. Therefore, Buffon's theory shares the difficulties encountered by modern tidal theories.

Let us just discuss one difficulty, which was pointed out by Nölke. If a mass of dimension a and density ρ is under the influence of the solar gravitational field, the differential rotation will dissipate the system. The gravitational self-attraction F_1 is given by the formula

$$F_1 \sim G\rho a^2, \tag{3}$$

while the solar gravitational field will produce a shearing force of the order of

$$F_2 \sim \frac{GM_0}{a}, \tag{4}$$

where M_0 is the solar mass. Comparing the two we see that

$$\frac{F_1}{F_2} \sim \frac{M}{M_0} \tag{5}$$

where M is the mass of the material torn from the sun. We see that indeed the shearing force will be too strong to allow for condensation by gravitational concentration. The period necessary for a nearly complete dissipation will be of the order of a few years and normal condensation is, therefore, also negligible, the more so because of the high temperature of the material (compare the arguments in Section VI). Therefore, if a collision had taken place it would result in the formation of a solar envelope.

III. The Nebular Hypothesis: Kant

In 1755, Kant published his cosmogonical ideas, which are mainly qualitative. A more quantitative formulation was given by du Ligondes in 1897. Kant starts his cosmogony by stating that it is certainly not irreverent to discuss possible consequences of the laws of nature. God has given us these laws and our brains to investigate their consequences. Laws of nature certainly do not exclude God's existence:

"There is obviously a God, because even in chaos nature cannot follow other than law and order."[6]

Kant assumed a universe filled more or less uniformly with gas. Regions with slightly larger density would act as sinks for matter and conglomerations of matter might be formed in this way. Kant had already suggested that the nebulae were really galaxies like our Milky Way.

Due to a concentration process, a nebular mass, the protosun, would be formed. Due to its rotation, it would flatten. In the disk, secondary mass concentrations would occur, at the center of which the planets should grow. The larger the planet, the larger the nebular concentration around it should be, and the more extensive its final satellite system would be. Kant explains the direct rotation of the planets in the following way. Consider a particle moving behind the protoplanet in the same (circular) orbit. Under the influence of the attraction of the planet, its velocity will increase and thus also the centrifugal force. It will move outward, away from the sun. Hence, if it collides, it will give the planet a direct rotation. A particle moving in front of the planet will be decelerated, move inwards and also increase the direct rotation.

The main reason why Kant's theory was not accepted as the final solution was that it was argued that gravitational concentration is impossible in the solar envelope. This follows from arguments similar to those given in the preceding section. However, recent developments seem to have given Kant's theory new life.

IV. The Nebular Hypothesis: Laplace [4]

In 1796, Laplace published, in a more or less popular book, his nebular hypothesis. It is often thought that Laplace put Kant's idea into scientific terms. However, the two theories were arrived at independently and have

---

[6] "Es ist ein Gott eben deswegen, weil die Natur auch selbst in Chaos nicht anders als regelmässig und ordentlich verfahren kann."

nothing in common except the same starting point: a gas nebula in the center of which the sun is situated. However, the properties of the two nebular are already different. Kant does not assume the nebula to be part of the sun, but Laplace assumes that the nebula, extending over the regions of the solar system, rotated together with the sun and really was a part of the sun, which at that time had larger dimensions that at present. The temperature of the whole nebula was supposed to be high at the beginning of the developments leading to the solar system.

The nebula will gradually cool and contract. While the contraction takes place, the rotational velocity will increase, until the centrifugal force at the equator becomes larger than the gravitational force, and part of the matter is left behind in the form of a ring. The main part of the nebula continued to contract, and a series of rings were thrown off in succession, and the planets, by an unspecified process, are supposed to have condensed from this system of concentric rings. Finally, the remainder of the central mass formed the sun.

Laplace's theory has generally been subjected to two types of criticism. The first one is that the Laplacian rings have no tendency to condense into planets; they might form a swarm of asteroids, but not larger bodies. The second difficulty that has been raised against the theory is that the total angular momentum of the solar system, even if concentrated in the sun, would produce a centrifugal force at the equator that is only about 5% of the gravitational force, and the sun would be in no danger of breaking up.

V. The Influence of Electric and Magnetic Effects

In 1912, Birkeland [9] introduced a new idea into the problem. He combined the fact that the sun has a magnetic moment and that it emits ions. These ions will spiral towards limiting circles. The radii of these circles will depend upon the ratio of the charge to the mass of the particles. In this way, a number of rings will be formed, consisting of different ions. However, a quantitative analysis of the process shows that the orbits of the ions are only slightly curved and that the limiting circles lie far outside the present solar system. Also, it is difficult to understand why, for instance, all four terrestrial planets are of approximately the same chemical constitution.

This interesting theory did not receive the attention it merited. The same happened to Berlage's theories, which certainly deserved a better fate, since they discussed many features that often pass unnoticed.

Berlage investigates in his first two theories[7] [19, 22, 23] the influence of the solar electric field. He starts from a situation where the sun is sur-

---

[7] His later theories are discussed in Section VIII.

rounded by an extensive envelope, which is flattened by rotation. Secondly, he assumes that the sun emits charged particles; in his first attempt he assumes the emission of negatively charged solar particles and positive ions; in his second theory he uses the observational fact that the sum emits positive ions and electrons.

In the first case, the sun will become positively charged, and around the sun a negative space charge will be formed. If we may neglect centrifugal forces, an ion of mass $m - Am_p$, where A is the atomic weight and m_p the proton mass, and of charge e, will be under the influence of three forces, and in the case of equilibrium we have

$$GM_0 m_p A + E(r)e = E_0 e \qquad (6)$$

where $-E(r)$ is the space charge inside a sphere of radius r, E_0 is the solar charge and M_0 is the solar mass.

Berlage assumes that ions of atomic weight A will act as condensation nuclei at a distance r from the sun which is given by equation (6); $E(r)$ is an increasing function of r and, therefore, r decreases with increasing A. After condensation has proceeded for some time, radiation pressure is supposed to push the condensation products outwards, still gaining mass, until the radiation force becomes only a small fraction of the gravitational force. Since the radiation pressure is proportional to the square of the radius r of the condensation, while the gravitational force is proportional to ρr^3, where ρ is the specific density of the condensation product, the condition for final equilibrium can be written in the form

$$\rho r^3 \propto r^2. \qquad (7)$$

If m is the mass of the condensation product, we get from equation (7):

$$M = k\rho^{-2} \qquad (8)$$

where k is constant.

The solution of equation (6) can be written in the form:

$$r = aq^{-A}. \qquad (9)$$

Berlage has now obtained a series of concentric rings, each ring consisting of one particular element. If p' is the fraction of atoms of atomic weight A in the original nebula, or p ($=p'A$), the fraction by weight, the mass of the planet corresponding to isotope A will be given by

$$M = k(p/A\rho^2) \qquad (10)$$

where k is again a constant. The density ρ is identified by Berlage with the density of the planet, and he finds the following series of isotopes which should have formed the planets:

$$A = 33, 32, 31, 30, 29, 28, 27, 26, 25. \qquad (11)$$

TABLE I

Planet	Element	A	p	ρ	M_{calc}	M_{obs}
Mercury	S	33	0.001	3.5	0.02	0.03
Venus	S	32	0.093	5.2	0.71	0.81
Earth	P	31	0.142	5.5	1	1
Mars	Si	30	0.26	4.1	3.4	0.11
Asteroids	Si	29	0.51	?	?	?
Jupiter	Si	28	24.94	2.5	940	318
Saturn	Al	27	7.50	2.0	455	95
Uranus	Mg	26	0.22	1.3	32.8	14.7
Neptune	Mg	25	0.22	1.2	40.2	17.3

In Table I the calculated and observed masses are compared, both expressed in the earth's mass as a unit. This table is reproduced from Berlage's monograph.

Since the values of A form a descending arithmetic series, equation (9) gives us the Titius–Bode law.

It hardly needs to be emphasized that there are many weird points in this theory and many points which cannot stand up against a quantitative analysis. To mention only a few: in equation (6) the centrifugal force is neglected; the series in equation (11) is certainly not the only possible one; the densities of the condensation nuclei are certainly less than those of the planets since the internal pressure of the planets will increase their average density. The most important point is, however, that in an envelope like the one considered by Berlage, ionization is negligible, thus rendering his whole analysis superfluous. Berlage assumes that the electric field of the planets will produce the satellite systems in a manner similar to the production of the planetary system through the influence of the solar electric field.

It must, however, be admitted that many of the theories recently proposed and discussed have at least as many weak points as Berlage's first theory and that the ideas in Berlage's theory are certainly sufficiently interesting to deserve a closer investigation. Berlage himself abandoned this theory because the assumption of the emission of solid particles by the sun proved it to be in contradiction to observational evidence.

In his second theory, Berlage again studies, under neglect of centrifugal forces, the motion of charged particles leaving the sun. Under certain simplifying assumptions, he finds the space charge $E(r)$ has a periodic character:

$$E(r) = k_1\sqrt{r}\left[a\cos\left(k_2\ln\frac{r}{r_0}\right) + b\sin\left(k_2\ln\frac{r}{r_0}\right) + c\right] \qquad (12)$$

where k_1, k_2, a, b, and c are constants. From equation (12) it follows that there are spheres on which the electric force is zero. The radii of these spheres will intersect the disk at circles, and the ratio of the radii of two consecutive circles will be given by the formula:

$$r_{n+1}/r_n = \exp(\pi/k_2) \tag{13}$$

which again gives us the Titius–Bode law.

On these circles of zero electric field strength, ions are supposed to assemble. Since supposedly all atoms spend part of their life as ions, rings of matter will form on the circles.

Berlage has thus again obtained Laplacian rings and the subsequent condensation is not discussed. Against this theory many objections can be raised. The most important one is again that ionization is negligible in a disk like the one considered by Berlage. Secondly, the main point in the theory is the explanation of the Titius–Bode law. However, in order to get the rings of matter at fixed places, the electric field has to be constant. This means that the emission of charged particles by the sun has to be constant. We know that at the present time the emission of charged particles from the sun is, however, highly variable. Since there is no reason for expecting such emission to have been constant at any time in the past, the foundation of Berlage's theory is destroyed. Berlage himself abandoned the second theory because it was not able to explain the formation of the satellite systems by a process analogous to the process responsible for the formation of the planetary system.

VI. Modern Tidal Theories

In most popular books that appeared two or three decades ago, the tidal theory has been pictured as the most promising of all theories about the origin of the solar system. As we saw in Section II, the idea goes back to Buffon. Since then, many other authors have tried to work with his theories. During the last century, Bickerton [5] suggested that an encounter between two stars also produced a nova-like explosion, with the eruption leading to the formation of the planets. In this century, Arrhenius [11] considered a head-on collision of two stars leading to one star and a gaseous filament, and See [8] considered the collision of two nebulae leading to one nebular protosun which subsequently captured the planets. The work of Chamberlin [6, 18] and Moulton [7] is perhaps better know. Their planetesimal theory considered an encounter between two stars in which a large tidal protuberance was raised on the surface of the sun facing the intruding star.

Owing to the expansion of the hot, compressed gases in this tidal protuberance, a series of great eruptions occurred in which clouds of matter were ejected. These clouds were supposed to be accelerated by the passing star and given a sidewards component to their motion, thus accounting for the large angular momentum in the planets.

As the clouds of matter cooled, liquid drops were supposed to have condensed out of them and solidified. The planets were supposed to have grown by an accumulation of these solid particles into larger bodies. The residual matter was supposed to act as a resisting medium that would reduce the eccentricities of the orbits of the planets and produce the present organization of the solar system.

Jeffreys [17] criticized the planetesimal hypothesis on the grounds that the planetesimals should collide frequently and with sufficiently high relative velocities so that volatilization would occur before the accretion into planets could have progressed very far. Both he [12, 14, 21] and Jeans [13, 15, 20] produced modified forms of the theory, and these are the ones that mainly shall be considered here. They postulated that the passage of the star close to the sun would cause one long filament of matter to be drawn out, and to break up into separate fragments, each subsequently condensing into a planet. They assumed that the filament would resemble a cigar, with the greatest density towards the middle, so that the largest planets would be the ones at medium distances from the sun. The satellites of the planets were supposed to have been produced by a partial breaking-up of the fragments on their first return to the vicinity of the sun. Jeans and Jeffreys also assumed that the resistance of the residual matter would round out the orbits of the planets, producing the near circles that exist today.

This idea is simple, and at first it seems that there is no difficulty in accounting for any observed distribution of angular momentum in the system. However, there are many difficulties. Before discussing the most serious difficulties, we shall mention a few minor ones.

The first difficulty lies in the explanation of the planetary rotation. Both the planets and the sun were at first supposed to have been set into rotation by matter that fell back into them after acquiring angular momentum from the passage of the intruding star. But such an idea does not withstand quantitative examination. It turns out that the amount of matter that must be supposed to fall back onto the planets or onto the sun is almost comparable to the masses of the sun or of the planets themselves. Furthermore, Jeans showed that the satellites of the planets could not have been formed from the primitive protoplanets by the tidal action of the sun.

This led Jeffreys to revive Buffon's original idea, that rather than having a close passage of two stars, there had been an actual grazing collision between them. This was still supposed to lead to the formation of a filament, and, owing to the viscosity of this filament, Jeffreys could show that a rotation of the right order of magnitude would ensue.

The next and greater difficulty is whether the resisting medium really can reduce the orbits of the planets to ones of small eccentricity. Nölke [23a] and Russell [27] have discussed this point and arrive at the conclusion that it seems doubtful whether the resisting medium is sufficiently effective.

The next difficulty lies in just the point where the tidal theory seems to score: the distribution of angular momentum. Russell has shown that if the encounter were responsible for the present distribution of angular momentum, one would expect large inner and small outer planets, in disagreement with observation.

The most serious difficulties are those pointed out by Nölke and by Spitzer [31]. Nölke's criticism was mentioned in the discussion of Buffon's theory, and we shall now briefly discuss Spitzer's arguments.

First of all, let us simplify the discussion by assuming that we may treat the filament as a spherical mass. Let us assume that the mass M is about 10^{30} gm (which may be too small but a larger mass will not change the final results as follows from Spitzer's more careful considerations), and that it had originally a density ρ_0. This density originally would be of the order of stellar densities, that is, ~ 1 gm cm^{-3} The temperature of the filament, T_0, must originally have been as high as $10^{6}°$K as Russell has pointed out: a mass sufficiently large to produce the planets must have come from the inner regions of the sun.

The internal energy W of the filament is thus at least equal to

$$W \sim kT_0(M/m_p). \tag{14}$$

The gravitational self-energy of the filament, U, will be of the order of magnitude

$$U \sim (GM^2/R) \tag{15}$$

where R is related to ρ_0 and M by

$$\rho_0 R^3 \sim M. \tag{16}$$

From equations (14) to (16) it follows that

$$(W/U) \sim (kT_0/\rho_0^{1/3}M^{2/3}Gm_p) \sim 10, \tag{17}$$

which means that the filament would expand to infinity unless it could lose its energy sufficiently fast.

Kramers and Burgers [41] have shown that the expansion essentially takes place with the velocity of sound:

$$V \sim (kT_0/m_p)^{1/2}. \tag{18}$$

In this way, the filament will have doubled its dimensions in a time τ_1 given by

$$\tau_1 \sim (R/V) \sim (Rm_p^{1/2}/(kT_0)^{1/2}) \sim 1 \text{ hour}!! \qquad (19)$$

On the other hand, the energy of the filament will be radiated away at a rate given by the total luminosity

$$L \sim R^2 a T_0^4 c, \qquad (20)$$

where a is Stefan–Boltzmann's constant. The period τ_2 during which the temperature will be decreased substantially is now given by

$$\tau_2 \sim (W/L) \sim (kM/m_p R^2 c a T_0^3). \qquad (21)$$

Comparing τ_1 and τ_2 we get:

$$(\tau_1/\tau_2) \sim (R^3 m_p^{3/2} c a T_0^{5/2}/k^{3/2}M) \sim 10^{-1}. \qquad (22)$$

From equation (22) we see that the loss of energy through radiation is so slow that the filament will have dissipated before it can cool down sufficiently so that condensation can start. Turbulence will probably act to increase still further the rate of dissipation. The rough estimate given here is borne out by the more careful analysis by Spitzer.

As Spitzer pointed out, the probable final situation would be an extended atmosphere surrounding the sun. This is the same situation as that from which most monistic theoris start and a tidal origin of the extended atmosphere seems rather far-fetched.

VII. The Binary and Triple Star Theories [28–30, 33, 34]

Because of the many difficulties encountered by the tidal theories, Russell proposed a solution where the sun was part of a binary system. The binary companion of the sun would then have undergone a close encounter with a third star. The encounter would result in a disruption of the binary system and the production of a gaseous filament. Lyttleton has investigated this possibility carefully. However, this theory has difficulties in explaining the origin of the satellite systems and, even more important, Spitzer's objections to the tidal theories are again valid in this case.

In 1941, Lyttleton suggested that the sun originally was part of a triple star, consisting of a close binary and the sun. Due to the accretion of interstellar material, the separation of the two companions of the sun will decrease. The two stars will finally combine into one mass. However, this mass will break up because of rotational instability. After this fission, the two parts will leave the system, producing a situation reminiscent of the situation met in Lyttleton's original theory after the breakup of the binary. The same objections apply, therefore.

VIII. A Revival of Kant's Theory [24–26, 32, 47, 48]

The most persistent of all modern scientists dealing with the problem of the origin of the solar system is probably Berlage. After a series of three papers dealing with his first two theories (Section V), Berlage published a series of seven papers. As Berlage wrote himself: "(The author) admits that in his odyssey through several attempts to attain a rational picture of the evolution of the planets, he was many times led astray." He continues: "But (the author) is now in the position to formulate a rather concise theory as a working basis." It will be seen that the first steps in this theory are identical with the first steps in the theories of Kant, von Weizsäcker, Kuiper, or ter Haar.

The basic idea of Berlage's theory is that a gaseous disk around the sun might spontaneously develop into a system of concentric rings. Berlage starts by proving that a gaseous envelope will develop into a disk due to rotation. Berlage assumes that there is no turbulence and that the mean molecular weight in the disk varies in such a way that the pressure in the disk is constant. Neither of these two assumptions is correct. The assumption of a varying molecular weight is made because Berlage assumes that only those elements which at present constitute the planets were present in the disk. The final result, a flattened disk, is, however, not affected by these assumptions.

Berlage supposes that the motion in the disk will be such that the dissipation of energy due to viscosity will be minimum. This seems a reasonable supposition. However, Berlage assumes independently that in the quasi-stable state of motion, viscous forces themselves should be minimum. It seems that this is hardly a new assumption, and certainly not one which can be assumed independently. From these assumptions Berlage goes on to deduce the mass distribution of the solar nebula:

$$\rho_s = \rho_0 \exp(-a\sqrt{s}) \tag{23}$$

where s is the distance from the axis of rotation, ρ_s is the density in the plane of the disk, and the two constants ρ_0 and a are determined from the total mass and angular momentum of the planetary system.

Berlage now discusses the further development of the disk. As long as the volume elements follow Kepler's third law, there will be a dissipation of energy through viscous interaction. Instead of assuming that this will result in a gradual dissipation of energy, Berlage assumes that rings of matter will be formed that rotate as a rigid body. These rings would then again be the Laplacian rings from which, by an unspecified process, the planets would condense. Berlage therefore looks for a possibility that this formation of concentric rings might take place spontaneously. He concludes that such a spontaneous formation of rings would indeed take place, although his analysis lacks mathematical rigor. Safronov, in Russia, has recently arrived at similar conclusions, although his analysis also lacks the necessary degree of mathematical rigor. At the present time, the question of such ring formation cannot be regarded as settled.

Berlage's analysis led him to the conclusion that the distance of the successive rings, and hence of the successive planets, would be given by the equation

$$\ln r_n - \ln r_{n-1} = \text{constant}, \qquad (24)$$

corresponding to the Titius–Bode law.

Berlage also discusses the masses of the planets following from his picture and he finds, indeed, an initial increase in mass with increasing distance from the sun and a subsequent decrease, in accordance with the observed mass distribution in the planetary system.

Berlage assumes that an encounter with another star is responsible for the present distribution of angular momentum but not for the existence of the gaseous envelope. The satellite systems should have been formed in a way analogous to the formation of the planetary system in envelopes around the planets.

As is seen from the above discussion, Berlage's last theory embodies ideas from many older theories. Let us end this discussion of Berlage's theories by quoting from his 1940 paper [32]: "It is a stimulating aspect of the account which we have tried to give that the solar system in successive stages of evolution could be identified with a Cartesian whirl, with Kant's disk and the rings of Laplace. Even Chamberlin and Moulton's planetesimals were met at a certain stage, whereas for Jeans' foreign star there might have been work to do at the moment of conception. It might have started the evolution, leaving the rest to be done spontaneously. At any rate, this beautifully ordered structure, which is our planetary system, is essentially self-made."

IX. Again the Solar Magnetic Field [35, 36, 43, 58]

Without being familiar with Birkeland's or Berlage's theories, Alfvén has investigated the influence of the solar magnetic field. There appeared to him to be two ways in which the solar magnetic field might have a great influence on the formation of the planetary system.

If one compares the magnetic force F_m on a proton moving in the earth's orbit with a velocity of a few kilometers per second, with the gravitational force F_g on the same proton, the first force is by far the larger.

$$F_m = evM/cr^3, \tag{25}$$

where e is the charge of the proton, v its velocity, M the solar magnetic moment, and r the distance from the sun. On the other hand, the gravitational force is given by

$$F_g = GM_0 m_p/r^2, \tag{26}$$

and their ratio is given by

$$F_m/F_g = evM/GM_0 m_p rc \sim 60,000. \tag{27}$$

The second reason for proposing this new theory was that the interaction of the solar magnetic moment with a surrounding ion cloud might reduce the solar angular momentum in as short a period as 10^6 years, according to calculations of Alfvén.

Alfvén's proposal was the following: suppose that the sun on its journey through space had met an ion cloud and was surrounded by it at a certain moment. If we may neglect the angular momentum of the cloud with respect to the sun, the atoms in the cloud will start falling towards the sun. Neglecting the initial potential and kinetic energy of these atoms, the kinetic energy T of the atoms will be given by

$$T = GM_0 m/r \tag{28}$$

where m is the mass of the atom and r the distance from the sun. Eventually this kinetic energy will have become so large that ionization by collision can take place. This will happen as soon as T is of the order of magnitude of the ionization energy $e\chi$

$$GM_0 m/r \sim e\chi. \tag{29}$$

The distance r_0 at which ionization starts will thus be given by

$$r_0 \sim (GM_0 m/e\chi) = 14 \times 10^{13}(A/\chi) \text{ cm}, \tag{30}$$

where A is the atomic weight of the atom considered and χ is measured in electron volts.

The idea is now that collisions are so frequent that ionization will really take place at a distance r_0 from the sun. Once an ion is formed, the movement towards the sun is stopped and the ion has to move along the magnetic lines of force until it reaches an equilibrium position in the equatorial plane of the sun. It should be borne in mind here that as soon as ionization has taken place the gravitational force on the ion may be neglected.

If originally the atoms are moving uniformly towards the sun, and if they are all ionized at the same distance r_0 from the sun, it is possible to calculate the ensuing mass distribution in the equatorial plane from the known shape of the lines of force. If $dm(r)$ is the mass between r and $r + dr$ from the sun, we have the following equation for $m(r)$:

$$\frac{dm(r)}{dr} = \frac{k}{r^2[1 - (r_0/r)]^{\frac{1}{2}}}, \tag{31}$$

where k is a constant.

For a representative ion, Alfvén assumes $A = 7$, $\chi = 12$ ev, and in this way obtains

$$r_0 \sim 10^{14} \text{ cm}, \tag{32}$$

which is about equal to Jupiter's mean distance from the sun.

The mass distribution given by equation (31) agrees roughly with the mass distribution in the series of the giant planets. Even if we accept Alfvén's process for a moment as being responsible for producing the material for the giant planets, we meet, however, with very serious difficulties in the case of the terrestrial planets. Even for hydrogen ($A = 1$, $\chi = 13.6$ ev), r_0 is far larger than the mean distance of Mercury from the sun. Alfvén suggests without giving any details—not even a qualitative discussion—that a smoke cloud might have met the sun. Through solar radiation, smoke particles might sublimate and the resulting atoms might become ionized at a distance from the sun much less than r_0.

Before discussing this part of Alfvén's theory critically, we should like to consider his condensation picture. Alfvén does not consider the Titius–Bode law, but instead introduces his $q - Q$ diagram, where q is the ratio of the mean distances of two neighboring planets (satellites) to the sun (primary), and Q is the ratio of their masses. Plotting all pairs of satellites and planets, Alfvén finds that one can distinguish two groups which he calls first and second families. The first family lies, according to Alfvén, in the $q - Q$ diagram on a curve where q increases with decreasing Q; the mean density of these bodies is less than 3 gm/cm³, and their gravitational self-energy lies within a certain interval. The curve representing the second family in the small $q - Q$ diagram shows increasing q with increasing Q; the mean density is larger than 3 gm/cm³ and the gravitational self-energy lies outside the interval occupied by the first family. The terrestrial planets belong to the second family, and the giant planets to the first family.

It must be remarked here that Alfvén's representation gives a distorted picture, since he uses a semi-logarithmic plot. If he had used a double logarithmic plot, all dots would have practically fallen on a line $q =$ constant, corresponding to the Titius–Bode law.

Alfvén tries to explain his $q - Q$ diagram by considering in some detail the condensation of the gaseous disk. Again we shall refrain from criticism until after a presentation of Alfvén's ideas. He has shown that after the ions are neutralized, they will move in ellipses with eccentricity 1/3. If we now assume that matter moving in such an ellipse will always be captured completely when colliding with other matter, we get the following picture of the condensation process in the plane of the disk.

Suppose that condensation starts at a distance r from the sun and that as the region of condensation moves inwards, matter at distances less than r becomes neutralized and starts moving in ellipses with eccentricity 1/3. These ellipses will flatten out into circles through collisions. The radius of these circles will be equal to $2r/3$, through conservation of angular momentum. The final result will, therefore, be a ring of condensed matter at a distance $2r_1/3$. Since, however, during this condensation process matter was swept up between r_1 and $2r_1/3$, with lower angular momentum per unit mass, the final ring of condensed matter will be situated at a distance r_2, somewhat less than $2r_1/3$. After this, a similar process starts, beginning at r_2 instead of at r_1, and so on. Condensation of the rings into planets is not discussed.

From this picture of the condensation process, we have

$$q = r_1/r_2 = r_2/r_3 = \cdots = \text{constant } (>1) \tag{33}$$

i.e., the ratio of the orbital radii of two neighboring planets is constant. It would appear that Alfvén has here derived the Titius–Bode law. This conclusion is not reached by Alfvén, however.

Alfvén now assumes that the mass distribution in the disk is given by the equation

$$dm/dr = hr^{n-1}, \tag{34}$$

where h and n are constants.

If we assume that all the mass of the planet finally situated at r_2 is condensed into the planet, we find for the mass of the planet, m:

$$m = \int_{r_2}^{r_1} dm = (h/n)(r_1{}^n - r_2{}^n). \tag{35}$$

From equation (35) it follows immediately, that as long as equations (33) and (34) are satisfied, the ratio of the masses of two consecutive planets Q is also a constant and given by

$$Q = q^n. \tag{36}$$

It seems therefore that as long as equation (34) is valid, the whole planetary (or satellite) system should be represented by *one* point in the $q - Q$ diagram.

Alfvén, however, proceeds as follows. The total angular momentum of the matter between r_1 and r_2 should be equal to the angular momentum of the planet:

$$mr^2 \left(\frac{GM_0}{r_2{}^3}\right)^{\frac{1}{2}} = \int_{r_2}^{r_1} r^2 \left(\frac{2GM_0}{3r^3}\right)^{\frac{1}{2}} dm = \frac{2}{3} \frac{h}{n + \frac{1}{2}} (r_1{}^{n+1/2} - r_2{}^{n+1/2}), \qquad (37)$$

where the factor $\sqrt{2/3}$ stems from the eccentricity of the orbits.

Hence,

$$m(r_2)^{\frac{1}{2}} = \tfrac{2}{3}[h/(n+\tfrac{1}{2})](r_1{}^{n+1/2} - r_2{}^{n+1/2}). \qquad (38)$$

Eliminating m, h, and n from equations (33), (35), (36), and (38), we get the following relation between q and Q:

$$(Q\sqrt{q} - 1)/(Q - 1) = \sqrt{2/3}\,[1 + (\ln q)/(2 \ln Q)]. \qquad (39)$$

In the case of an outward moving condensation, equation (39) has to be replaced by

$$(Q\sqrt{q} - 1)/(Q\sqrt{q} - \sqrt{q}) = \sqrt{\tfrac{3}{4}}\,[1 - (\ln q)/(2 \ln Q)]. \qquad (40)$$

The curves in the $q - Q$ diagram representing equations (39) and (40) agree to some extent with the observational curves.

Let us now consider Alfvén's ideas more critically. First of all, let us consider his condensation picture. We mentioned already that if equation (34) is valid, the planetary or satellite system would be represented by *one point* in the $q - Q$ diagram. If, however, equation (34) is not valid, then equations (35) and (38) are no longer correct, and the equations (39) and (40) have no basis. The only curve in the $q - Q$ diagram corresponding to a planetary system would be a straight line parallel to the Q-axis (equation 33) and not the curves corresponding to equations (39) and (40).

Even apart from these points, there seems to be no physical basis for the condensation picture given by Alfvén. One should investigate the dynamics of the disk hydrodynamically and not by considering the separate orbits of the various particles as has been done by Alfvén.

Let us now consider the basic ideas of Alfvén's theory. He assumes that electromagnetic effects have played an important role in the development of the solar system. Indeed, one of his postulates is that the dipole moment of the sun is some 10^5 times as great as the present one. In his original picture, Alfvén supposes that the atoms will become ionized as soon as their kinetic energy has become as large as their ionization energy. This picture is not consistent since it suposes on the one hand that the atoms will come from very large distances from the sun without suffering collisions, so that their kinetic energy is equal to the total gain of potential energy. On the other hand, Alfvén assumes that collisions are so frequent that the atoms are ionized as soon as their kinetic energy is large enough for ionization by collisions. Thus, at the same time, the mean free path has to be both large and small as compared with the dimensions of the solar system. Since even in average interstellar clouds the mean free path is not large as compared to the dimensions of the solar system, it follows that the mechanism which is the basis of Alfvén's calculations is impossible.

X. The Supernova Hypothesis [37, 40, 42]

Inspired by Lyttleton's theories, Hoyle investigated the case where a binary companion of the sun became a supernova. The material of the planetary system was postulated to have been provided by the gaseous shells expelled during the supernova outburst. This theory requires several important conditions to be satisfied by the outburst.

The recoil on the supernova due to the outburst must be sufficiently large to break up the binary system. Very little is known about the asymmetry of supernova explosions, but it does not seem impossible that this requirement might be met.

The mass of the diffuse gaseous material thrown off in the outburst must be large compared with the total mass of the planets, since the high average velocity of expulsion makes it certain that the sun can only capture a small fraction of the total mass thrown off by the supernova. The observed velocities of expansion of supernova shells are some two orders of magnitude greater than the velocity of escape from the sun at one astronomical unit. Hoyle assumes that in the later stages of the outburst the velocities are sufficiently small and the ejection of matter still sufficiently large to allow the sun to capture sufficient material to produce the planetary system.

The heating of the diffuse material that is captured by the sun must not lead to thermal velocities exceeding the escape velocity from the sun. According to Hoyle's analysis, the supernova stays in the immediate neighborhood of the sun for at least three years. Since the surface temperature of the supernova remnant will probably lie in the range 10^5 to $10^{6}°K$, the diffuse material will certainly be kept at a high temperature. Also, a significant fraction of the energy of the supernova appears to go into the production of high-energy particles. Large heating effects must be expected when these high-energy particles traverse any diffuse material.

The material expelled from the supernova was obviously at a high temperature originally. Spitzer's objections to planetary condensation, therefore, apply. Hence, the most that might be expected to result from the process considered by Hoyle would be the production of a solar nebula.

XI. The Role of Turbulence [38, 44, 45]

In a paper dedicated to Sommerfeld on the occasion of his 75th birthday, von Weizsäcker has revived ideas of Descartes' and Kant's theories. He assumes that after the sun was formed it still was surrounded by an extended envelope. Because of the rotation of this envelope, it will flatten. The mean density in the disk will be approximately 10^{-10} gm/cm^3 and the total mass will be about one-tenth of a solar mass. The constitution of the disk is supposed to be the same as that of the sun. The Reynolds number in the disk will be about 10^{11}. Hence von Weizsäcker concludes that the motion in the disk will be turbulent.

Von Weizsäcker argues in the following way: pressure and friction forces will be small compared with the gravitational force, so that we may expect a more or less regular pattern of currents, which is mainly regulated by gravitation, and as long as gravitation is the only force working, there is no energy loss.

If we take into account only gravitation, every mass element will describe a Keplerian orbit. Let us describe the movement of the mass element in a coordinate system moving uniformly around the sun, with a period equal to the period of the mass element considered. The movement in the rotating system is again periodic and the representative point in the new system of reference describes a closed curve. This curve should be a point, if the orbit were a circle.

If the Keplerian orbit has a small eccentricity, the closed curve in the rotating system of reference will be an ellipse with a ratio of axes 2:1. The major axis of this ellipse is perpendicular to the major axis of the Keplerian orbit. If the motion in the Keplerian orbit is counterclockwise, the motion in the closed curve is clockwise. For larger eccentricities, the curve is no longer an ellipse but is a more complicated figure, and its size increases as the eccentricity increases. The rotational period of the whole closed curve in the rotating system increases with increasing distance from the sun, according to the third Keplerian law.

The next step is the composition of a vortex from an assembly of mass elements with the same major axis, but different eccentricities. Since the period of the mass element around the sun is determined by its major axis, all these mass elements will have the same period around the sun. Inside such a vortex there will be no friction and also no pressure gradients, if we choose the same density everywhere in the vortex. Since all mass elements are moving along Keplerian orbits, there is no work done against gravitation, so that the whole vortex is moving along without energy loss. The angular velocity of this vortex in its movement around the sun is determined by the distance of its center from the sun.

We can now consider the situation where several of these vortices have been formed and some matter, still moving in Keplerian orbits, is left out. Two vortices at different distances from the sun will collide, if they meet at all, due to their different angular velocities as will matter, not yet included in the vortex.

Under what circumstances can matter be incorporated into a vortex? If two mass points, moving along different Keplerian orbits, collided, they can move on together along a new ellipse. For the collision of two vortices, the situation is different, however. For instance, two vortices at the same distance from the sun cannot be united to form one larger vortex. Since pressure equilibrium has to be maintained, the material of one of the two vortices has to come at the outside of the other vortex. If the energy is conserved, the distance of the vortices from the sun cannot be changed. Now, the total angular momentum depends on the eccentricity as $(1 - e^2)^{1/2}$. Therefore, the total angular momentum of the two vortices should be decreased if the above process should take place. We see that the three requirements—conservation of energy, conservation of angular momentum, and pressure equilibrium—cannot be met at the same time.

Let us now consider a very small vortex. The particles at its outside, the orbits of which have the maximum eccentricity in the vortex, will have orbits characterized by a small eccentricity. When this vortex meets a particle with, say, the same energy, the chances are that the eccentricity of that particle will be larger than the maximum eccentricity in the vortex. This particle can thus be captured by the vortex. In this way, smaller vortices have a tendency to grow. But the growth of larger vortices is more difficult.

In general, a vortex can only absorb particles whose angular momentum is less than a certain value. If the major axis of the particle is the same as that of the particles in the vortex, this value is equal to the minimum angular momentum in the vortex. Also, we see that a vortex can capture more easily those particles with larger major axes and less easily those particles with smaller major axes.

It follows from this picture that a limit for the magnitude of the vortices must exist corresponding to a situation where the number of particles coming into the vortex during a time is equal to the number of particles carried off by colliding particles, which are not captured. This limiting magnitude will be independent of the distance from the sun and the corresponding limiting eccentricity, e_{max}, will not be small compared with unity.

If we now look into the further development of the vortices, we see that two vortices with the same distance from the sun can move around the sun without interference. If, however, their distances from the sun are different, they will collide, and since they cannot unite or pass through each other, they have to exchange energy and angular momentum until they can pass each other.

In this way, we may expect a final quasi-stable arrangement of vortices, where there are rings, each of them consisting of a number of vortices, touching each other. This means that e_{max} is restricted to a few possible values, corresponding to an integral number of vortices in a ring. Von Weizsäcker suggested there would be five vortices in a ring, since in this way he could obtain a satisfactory representation of the relative distances of the planets. This was his derivation of the Titius-Bode Law. Since e_{max} should be independent of the distance from the sun, we should expect the number of vortices in each ring to be the same throughout the disk. The angular velocities of the various rings are different.

One might wonder how this regular pattern of vortices can be reconciled with the fact that the motion in the disk is turbulent. Kuiper has argued that one should expect an irregular pattern of vortices rather than the one postulated by von Weizsäcker. However, this does not follow from hydro-dynamic considerations. The spectrum of the eddies may normally be expected to follow the relation of Kolmogoroff, but such a spectrum cannot be expected to hold at the limiting values of the highest and lowest wave numbers of the eddies. Moreover, it must never be forgotten that external circumstances will determine the spectrum for the largest eddies. Since in the solar disk the gravitational force is by far the most, von Weizsäcker argues that this force should be important in establishing the pattern of the largest eddies. In von Weizsäcker's picture the dissipation due to viscous forces is very small in the vortices themselves. Dissipation will mainly take place along the separating circles between vortices. The difference in linear velocities of the two rings at such a circle is indeed very large. If r is the distance of the separating ring from the sun, then the velocities of the inner and outer vortices at the separating ring is given by:

$$v_{inner} = \left[(GM_0/r)(1 - e_{max}) \right]^{\frac{1}{2}}. \tag{41}$$

$$v_{outer} = \left[(GM_0/r)(1 + e_{max}) \right]^{\frac{1}{2}}. \tag{42}$$

For example, if r is the distance of Jupiter from the sun, and $e_{max} = 1/3$, then the difference of velocity is of the order of 3 km/sec.

These large relative velocities will give rise to turbulence, and hence to secondary eddies along the separating circles. Since $v_{inner} < v_{outer}$, the rotation in these eddies will again be counterclockwise.

These secondary or "roller bearing" eddies have no tendency to grow, since they consume energy, but they may well by their "roller bearings" character be the agents maintaining the configuration of the large vortices.

The total mass of the "roller bearing" eddies is about one-fifth of the total mass of the disk; the ratio of the total matter in the disk to the matter in the large vortices is approximately given by the ratio of the area of the rectangle circumscribed around an ellipse to the area of the ellipse, i.e., $4:\pi$ or about $5:4$.

However, this theory certainly has to be revised since undisturbed Kepler orbits are out of the question. One has to consider the motion not from the point of view of the mechanics of independent particles but from a hydrodynamical one. Von Weizsäcker estimates the lifetime of the disk to be 10^7 or 10^8 years, but this is probably much too large in terms of a more realistic turbulence theory. The dissipation of energy is supplied by part of the matter which falls onto the sun, thus gaining gravitational energy. Von Weizsäcker assumes that the matter falling onto the sun has zero angular momentum, while the angular momentum is carried away by matter flying into infinity. In this way, he hopes to account for the slow rotation of the sun. It seems more likely, however, that as matter slowly spirals into the sun it will join with the Kepler orbital velocity at the equator of the sun, thus in fact increasing the sun's angular momentum.

Von Weizsäcker's idea of the condensation process is that in the gas there will always be nuclei for condensation. The larger nuclei will increase in size by capturing smaller particles. If two particles of comparable size collide, they will evaporate, but if the sizes are very different, they will fuse into one large particle. In this way, we have the first stage of growth of the particles, the stage of the straightforward capture of smaller particles by large nuclei. As soon as the particle has passed a certain critical size, the straightforward capture gives place to gravitational capture, which is the second and last stage of the growth of the body. Growth during the first stage is much slower than during the last stage. At first, the linear dimensions increase linearly with time, but during the final stage the particle can reach infinite dimensions, if the gas should be inexhaustible, during a time interval which is only one-third of the interval needed to arrive at the beginning of the final stage. The times in question are approximately 10^8 years, which should thus be the time necessary to build bodies of planetary dimensions.

The above estimates are made under the assumption that the not too large particles will share in the turbulent motion. In that case, we may expect the condensation to take place mainly in those regions where the mean free path of the turbulence is small, since the number of collisions will be largest there. Therefore, we should expect the condensation to take place in the "roller bearings." Since the "roller bearing" eddies are on the circle separating the major eddy systems, then we have seen that they should be spaced according to the Titius-Bode law, and the direct rotation of the "roller bearings" will lead to a direct rotation of the planets. We shall give here an estimate of the mean free path of the solid particles. If u_s is the relative velocity of the solid particles with respect to the medium, the loss of momentum of the particle in an interval dt is given by:

$$m_s\,du_s = -\pi r^2 \rho_g u_s^2\,dt, \tag{43}$$

where ρ_g is the gas density, $m_s = (4\pi/3)r^3\rho_0$ is the mass of the particle, r is the radius of the particle, and ρ_0 is the density of the particle.

For the mean free path, λ, we may take the distance traveled in an interval in which the particle's loss of momentum is as large as its original momentum. In this way, we get:

$$\lambda = \frac{m_s u_s}{\pi r^2 \rho_g u_s^2}; \qquad u_s = \frac{4}{3}\frac{\rho_0}{\rho_g}r, \tag{44}$$

which gives us, with $\rho_0 \sim 1$ gm/cm^3 and $\rho_g \sim 10^{-10}$ gm/cm^3:

$$\lambda \sim 10^{10}r. \tag{45}$$

From equation (44) we see that particles up to $r = 10^{-3}$ cm take part in the turbulence of both the large vortices and the "roller bearings." Particles, however, with r larger than 10^{-3} cm and not too large, are not carried along by the "roller bearings," but they can be carried along by the large vortices. This means an enhanced probability for growth in the "roller bearings" since the large particles ($r > 10^{-3}$ cm) are now more or less stationary, and so the relative velocity of these with respect to the smaller particles will be larger than in the case where both are carried along.

The principal difficulty with this or any similar hypothesis of growth by collisional accretion is the difficulty of finding a plausible set of conditions in which such accretion will occur. One needs to have some kind of stickiness between the colliding surfaces. One way of having such stickiness is to have the temperature of the particles very close to the melting point of one of the principal constituents. However, owing to this effect we would expect collisional accretion to occur only in a few selected regions of the solar nebula. Another form of stickiness would be a "vacuum welding" process, similar to that which occurs when two very clean metals touch in a vacuum. The main reason why this does not occur in air is that the metal surfaces acquire a thin oxide film in the air, which is not subject to vacuum welding. But, as Urey has shown, we may expect the particles present in the solar nebula to consist principally of metallic oxides and silicates. These probably would not have a tendency toward vacuum welding. Thus, clearly, processes of collisional accumulation must be far more complex than was theorized by von Weizsäcker.

XII. The Dust-Cloud Hypothesis [46, 49]

In connection with a dust-cloud hypothesis for the formation of stars that was under consideration in 1947, Whipple proposed a theory for the origin of the solar system. In his picture a smoke cloud with a radius of about 30,000 astronomical units and a mass of about one solar mass is contracting and producing the sun. The angular momentum of this cloud is supposed to be negligible, thus accounting for the small angular momentum of the sun. This smoke cloud captures a smaller smoke cloud possessing angular momentum with respect to the original cloud. In this secondary condensation planets are formed that from the beginning possess the necessary angular momentum, while the protosun itself possesses negligible angular momentum. It seems therefore that this theory has to be classified as a dualistic theory, although it comes very close to being monistic.

Whipple estimates the time of collapse of a smoke and gas cloud like the one considered here (radius of about 5×10^{17} cm, mean density of about 10^{-21} gm/cm^3) to be about 10^8 years. The collapse starts slowly and increases its rate in the later stages.

Whipple gives the following tentative qualitative explanations for the characteristics of the solar system. He assumes that a small group of partially condensed clouds were captured by, or developed in, the original cloud, and that they then spiraled inward by accretion to be left in approximately the orbits of the present planets, when the main cloud underwent its final rapid collapse. Thus he expects planets to be formed; their orbits would be nearly circular because accretion will reduce the eccentricity due to the influence of the resisting medium. The orbital orientations would be similar, because the small-cloud group was originally small compared to the large cloud, and the motions would be in a common direction. Whipple shows that a direct rotation of the planets will be the result of accretion in a cloud in which the density decreases from the center. He explains the slow direct rotation of the sun by the capture of a few small clouds which did not develop into planets. In order to explain the differences between the terrestrial and giant planets, Whipple suggests that, due to accretion, the protoplanets might have been heated up to such high temperatures that the more volatile compounds were lost. Since the orbital velocity decreases with increasing distance from the sun, and also the density in the protosun, this effect might have been more effective for the terrestrial planets than for the giant ones.

This theory is an interesting attempt to introduce new chemical and physical processes into a consideration of the origin of the solar system. Its weakness as a theory lies in the fact that practically all of the final regularities of the solar system that Whipple wishes to explain are introduced as a *priori* assumptions. Most of his hypotheses are not supported by quantitative calculations. Because of these weaknesses, Whipple's theory did not gain wide acceptance, and the significance of his concern with the basic physics and chemistry of the formation of the solar system was not appreciated.

XIII. Gravitational Instability in the Solar Nebula [51, 54, 55, 57]

Kuiper was attracted by von Weizsäcker's ideas concerning a turbulent solar nebula, although he argues that the large, regular vortices of von Weizsäcker would be impossible. Instead, Kuiper suggested that large gravitational instabilities might occur in such a nebula.

Let us consider a spherical mass of density ρ, mass M, and with a radius R, and a distance r from the sun. Due to the gravitational force of the sun, there will be a shearing force F_s acting on this mass. This force is given by the equation

$$F_s \sim (GM_0/r^3)R. \tag{46}$$

The self-gravitational force F_g on the other hand is

$$F_g \sim (GM/R) \sim G\rho R. \tag{47}$$

The mass is stable and can contract if $F_s < F_g$ or

$$\rho > (M_0/r^3) \sim 10^{-6}r^{-3} \text{ gm/cm}^3, \tag{48}$$

where r is expressed in astronomical units. The density on the right-hand side of equation (48) is called the Roche density.

Kuiper postulated that the Roche density was exceeded in large parts of the primitive solar nebula. He concluded that gas in such regions would thus be stable against tidal shear by the sun, and hence that it could become gravitationally unstable and condense. There are several difficulties with this hypothesis. First, if the solar nebula exceeds the Roche density over much of its area, then there will be important additional shearing effects due to the mass of the nebula itself. Secondly, it is not sufficient to assume that gravitational instability automatically follows from stability against shear. It is also necessary to show that the internal energy of a condensing mass of gas will be appropriately less than the gravitational potential energy of the system. No fully satisfactory theory of such gravitational instability has yet been published.

Kuiper goes on to assume that there will be one large protoplanet formed for each of the present planets, except possibly in the asteroid belt, where many smaller protoplanets might have been formed. These protoplanets are large and initially nearly touching. They have the solar composition.

As the protoplanets contract, much of the condensable mass is supposed to collect at the center, forming a planet, and some of the mass collects into the satellites revolving around such a planet. The large amount of noncondensable gas is eventually dissipated by the action of a bombardment by particles ejected from the sun, the solar wind.

There are many difficulties with this condensation picture. As the Russian scientist, Ruskol, has shown, very little dissipation of such giant protoplanets should be expected during the age of the solar system. If this picture were correct, one would also expect the earth to contain very much more of the heavy rare gases in its atmosphere than it does.

XIV. An Extension of von Weizsäker's Theory [50, 52]

Ter Haar criticized a number of points in von Weizsäcker's picture and undertook to investigate them more thoroughly. He discarded the large, regular turbulent eddies of von Weizsäcker, and concluded that a random turbulence would lead to a very thick solar nebula. Because of the very thick nebula, he concluded that gravitational instability would nowhere occur. Hence the planets must have formed by collisional accretion.

Ter Haar pointed out that the inner parts of the solar nebula would be considerably hotter than the outer parts, and hence only metallic compounds were likely to condense in the inner part, while practically all compounds, including the very abundant ices, would condense in the outer parts of the nebula. Because of the much larger amounts of material available for accumulation, he thus expected bodies to grow more rapidly in the outer parts, and to reach the stage of gravitational accretion before the nebula would dissipate. Such a stage would not be reached in the inner parts of the nebula. However, the principal difficulty with the picture was that the time available for condensation before turbulent dissipation of the nebula turned out to be much too small, approximately 1000 years. This is a consequence of the randomness of the turbulence assumed relative to von Weizsäcker's picture.

This short lifetime is a basic difficulty with any picture of the solar nebula that is dominated by turbulent processes. It is assumed that the gas is turbulent because the Reynolds number is high. It is also assumed that the largest eddies have dimensions not too much smaller than the scale length of the system. However, as E. N. Parker has shown, such a picture would predict that there should be some very large scale eddies in the interstellar gas of our own galaxy, which would lead to the dissipation of such gas in a time very short compared to the age of the galaxy. This is plainly not observed to be happening. The difficulty appears to be that there must be some definite form of energy input to the largest eddies, which then pass this energy down through a hierarchy of smaller and smaller eddies until the energy is finally dissipated as heat. The shear represented by the Kepler motion of the gas in orbits about the sun or about the galaxy does not seem to be a suitable source of input of dynamical energy. Hence, if one forms a solar nebula containing much turbulence, one should expect that this turbulent energy will be rapidly dissipated as heat, but that the nebula will not be physically dissipated during this process. In order to maintain turbulence within such a gas, one needs to postulate some additional physical processes that can give an input of turbulent energy to the largest scale eddies, but the shear due to differential rotation in a gravitational field does not seem suitable for this purpose.

XV. The Russian School of Cosmogony [59]

The year 1943 was marked not only by von Weizsäcker's cosmogonic proposals, but also by those of the Russian scientist, O. J. Schmidt, although Western scientists did not generally become aware of these latter proposals until much later. Schmidt assumed that the sun captured a swarm of small particles and bodies from interstellar clouds. These were assumed to grow to form planetary bodies by collisional accretion. He assumed that the Titius–Bode law resulted from nothing more than the competition between accumulating mass centers for materials swarming in space. Schmidt argued that if two planetary nuclei were formed fairly close together in space, then they would quickly sweep up the matter in the immediate vicinity. The growth of the nucleus that was closer to the sun would then depend mainly upon capturing material lying in orbits somewhat closer to the sun, which would cause the nucleus to move to a smaller orbit. Similarly, the outer body would mainly capture the material lying in outer orbits, and hence would tend to move outwards. It may readily be shown that if the binding energy of the material in each body which beinds it to the sun remains the same, and the angular momentum is conserved, then each body must rotate in a direct sense.

In 1950, two other Russian scientists, L. Gurevich and A. Lebedinsky, proposed a modification of Schmidt's picture. They suggested that the sun did not capture the particles from which the planets accumulated directly, but that these particles were formed in a gas cloud surrounding the sun. In the region close to the sun, the heat from the sun would allow only nonvolatile materials to condense into particles which could accumulate into planets. However, farther out, the nebula may have been very much colder, thus allowing volatile material to condense, and hence to form the giant planets of different composition. The volatile material is far more abundant in space than the nonvolatile material.

These ideas caused Schmidt to modify his proposal to that of a capture by the sun of a combination gas-dust cloud. However, he remarked that the essential features of his picture would remain the same had the gas and dust arisen as a result of the common formation process for both the sun and the planets.

Schmidt's picture of the accumulation processes is as follows. Friction of the dust particles with the gas is supposed to cause the particles to accumulate as a very thin disk in the equatorial plane. It then accumulates into asteroidal-sized bodies, possibly via collisional accumulation, but more likely from a local gravitational instability of the dust particles themselves. As the bodies grew in size, their originally circular orbits would become changed to elliptical ones, due to perturbations during close passages with other asteroidal-sized bodies. As the orbits became more elliptical, the probability of close encounters and collisions increased. The collisions would sometimes result in combinations and sometimes in fragmentations of the asteroidal-sized bodies. In the long run, we are supposed to wind up with a few major planets and some remaining asteroidal-sized bodies between the orbits of Mars and Jupiter.

There are, of course, many questions of detail, and even difficulties, associated with this general picture. A school of cosmogony grew up around O. J. Schmidt and continued to work following his death. There has been an extensive series of publications on many aspects of the solar system cosmogony emanating from this school. Among the investigators we may mention B. J. Levin, V. S. Safronov, E. Ruskol, and H. A. Lubimova. Many of these activities are centered in the O. J. Schmidt Institute of the Physics of the Earth, one of the institutes of the Academy of Sciences of the U.S.S.R.

XVI. Evidence from the Meteorites [53, 56]

An important new direction in cosmogonical research was established in the early 1950's by H. C. Urey. He was concerned not so much with the basic regularities in the solar system, whose explanation we have been seeking, but rather he was concerned with trying to deduce the conditions, or at least some limitations upon the conditions, that could give rise to the observed physical and chemical properties of the meteorites.

Meteorites occur in a wide variety of types, of which the two main broad classes are irons and stones. They are obviously fragments of larger bodies in space, and most investigators assume that they result from collisions of asteroidal bodies, although Urey has suggested that some of them may be chips from the moon. Hence, by studying meteorites, we are probably getting far more detailed information about the interior of smaller bodies in space than we are likely to obtain about the interior of the earth for a long time to come. Evidently a record of much of the early formative stages of the solar system is preserved in such bodies.

One of Urey's early and very fruitful hypotheses was that the chondrites were average samples of the nonvolatile material in the solar system. The chondrites are a common form of stony meteorite that contains small, round inclusions, called chondrules. From this assumption, Urey and H. E. Suess constructed a "cosmic" abundance distribution of the elements, in which they interpolated the abundances of the volatile elements and those for which there were not good measurements in meteorites. These interpolations were carried out with attention paid to nuclear regularities. This abundance table has been of great use in the construction of the theory of the origin of the elements by nuclear reactions in stellar interiors. It has, in fact, been so successful in this regard, that the interest in the abundances of the elements in chondrites now centers on the way in which abundances either differ from what appears to be the proper cosmic abundance distribution, or in the variations in the abundances of certain elements from one chondritic sample to another. A further obvious conclusion from this is that the parent bodies of the meteorites were subjected to much less heating and chemical differentiation than the material in the earth.

Another interesting conclusion that can be drawn from abundance studies is that there must be significant abundance differences between the meteorites and the moon. This follows from the consideration that the mean density of the moon is less than that of chondritic meteorites, despite the fact that there will be some compressional increase in the density of the moon, as compared to an object which has no internal pressure. It has been suggested that this difference might arise from the presence of significant quantities of water or graphite upon the moon, but Urey tends to discount these ideas on chemical grounds and to suggest instead that the moon contains less iron than the chondrites. This idea is supported by the fact that the sun appears to have less iron than either its neighbors or the chondrites.

Other evidence concerning composition comes from calculations of heating in the lunar interior. Several years ago, Urey concluded that if the moon possessed a chondritic composition, then the heat evolved from K^{40} would be sufficient to have melted the moon's interior extensively. Because of the small thermal conductivity of rocky material, this heat would not have had a chance to escape within the age of the solar system. But the figure of the moon shows large departures from hydrostatic equilibrium, and it is hard to see how this can be the case if the interior of the moon is molten. Thus, it seems that the moon may well be deficient in potassium as compared with the chondrites. This is consistent with the observation of P. Gast, who concluded from a study of the isotopic composition of terrestrial strontium that the earth was deficient in rubidium relative to thechondritic meteorites. Rubidium and potassium are chemically similar elements.

Another very interesting problem is the basic question of how the asteroids themselves were heated, assuming that the asteroids were the meteorite parent bodies. From the fact that some meteorites contain diamonds, which can only be formed under steady-state conditions at high pressures, Urey had concluded that the meteorite parent bodies must have been of lunar size, and that the asteroids must have resulted from a break-up of these primary objects and a reaccumulation into smaller secondary objects. However, Fish, Goles, and Anders suggested instead that the asteroids must have been primary objects and that their interiors required a source of heating that would be at least sufficient to melt iron. Lipschutz and Anders got around the diamond problem by showing that the diamonds in meteorites were almost certainly formed by shock impact rather than under steady-state conditions. But Anders had concluded from the study of argon in meteorites that the meteorite parent bodies could not have remained at a high temperature during the age of the solar system, but must have cooled off to less than $200°K$ rather early in the history of the solar system. This can only occur if the meteorite parent bodies are rather small. But the melting of the material in the interior of the small body requires a rather intense heat source. Hence, Fish, Goles, and Anders suggested that extinct radioactivities may have been responsible for doing this. They suggested that Al^{26} was the most likely source of the extinct radioactivity, and they assumed that it would have to be left over from the radioactivity present in the interstellar gas from which a condensation to form the solar system would start. Subsequently, the possibility has arisen that the Al^{26} might be produced by high-energy spallation reactions in a primitive solar nebula. Although Urey was actually the first to suggest that Al^{26} might have been important as a heat source in the early history of the solar system, the suggestion of Fish, Goles, and Anders, nevertheless, left him unhappy. He objected to the accumulation of iron in the core of an asteroidal body, as in the model of Fish, Goles, and Anders, since evidence from many of the iron meteorites shows that they contain large holes that cannot have been produced by heating during their passage through the atmosphere but must mark an interface between iron and stony material in the meteorite parent body. It also appears to him that the suggestion of Fish, Goles, and Anders would aggravate the problem of a heating in the interior of the moon, since the amount of potassium in ordinary chondritic composition already seems to provide too much heat for the interior of the moon.

Therefore, Urey has postulated that a rather large solar nebula was formed about the sun during its condensation process from the interstellar medium, and that small portions of this solar nebula became gravitationally unstable. From a formula due to Ledoux, not strictly applicable to this problem, Urey has concluded that the size of the gas spheres that become gravitationally unstable in such a solar nebula probably corresponds to an abundance of nonvolatile constituents equal to approximately the mass of the moon. During the contraction of such gravitationally unstable gas clouds, the temperature in the central regions would increase, and Urey believes this to be the probably source of melting of the materials that collect at the center. During subsequent collisions, or near collisions, of such bodies, the gas is supposed to be dissipated, leaving behind the solids collected at the center, which can then eventually be collected into the planets. In Urey's view, the moon is one of these surviving cores of a gravitationally unstable sphere of gas.

Needless to say, there are a great many unsolved problems associated with this set of postulates by Urey. However, their value lies in the fact that it is now generally recognized that a theory of the origin of the solar system cannot consider only the traditional regularities upon which past theories have been built, but also must take into account the very complex history of the chemistry and physics of the meteorites. In recent years ideas in the field of meteorite cosmogony have been in a state of rapid flux, and it is unlikely that any of the recent suggestions will survive the passage of time in a form at all close to the present ones. It may be seen from the preceding discussion that a great many people are now actively working upon these problems, and with the continuing accumulation of physical and chemical data a rapid rate of progress can be expected to continue.

XVII. Recent Developments and Future Prospects

Let us consider for a moment the situation, and ask why there are so many theories while apparently none is satisfactory. The absence of a satisfactory theory is clearly not due to a lack of interest in the problem; indeed, such interest has been rapidly mounting in recent years. However, it is instructive to ask, why are there so many theories that all claim to have solved the problem? The reason is that practically all theories lack a quantitative basis. Practically all theories are qualitative, showing possible processes that might lead to our planetary system. However, they do not consider the question of whether the proposed processes can also quantitatively account for the formation of the planets. This absence of a quantitative analysis is very often concealed by a more or less quantitative analysis of a few details, without, however, specifying the value of important constants entering into the calculations. It cannot be emphasized too often, or too strongly, that cosmogony can also be treated by the same rigorous analytical methods that have been so successful in other branches of astrophysics.

At the present time, our quantitative information about the solar system and its early history is rapidly increasing in quantity. Much of this information comes from the new science of meteoritics, as discussed in the last section. Much of it comes from the new types of physical measurements that are giving us information about the surfaces and atmospheres of the moon and other planets. Much of it comes from a study of star formation and from study of stellar evolution generally. With the exploration of the moon and planets imminent, we may soon expect a huge flood of new factual material pertaining to the problem. In order to gain acceptance, new theories of the origin of the solar system must meet and satisfy a tremendous number of new boundary conditions.

The results of some current thinking on these problems are displayed in the following chapters of this book. It will be observed that research on solar system cosmogony is continuing to take entirely new paths, and it is hoped that these new paths will lead to a more satisfactory quantitative basis for some final ensuing theory.

One of these new paths is the renewed interest in star formation and its influence on the formation of the planetary system. In recent years, astrophysical research has shown that our galaxy is much older than our solar system, and also that star formation is a process that continues to this day. Hence, modern cosmogonists tend to believe that some form of monistic theory must be the correct one, and probably the sun and the planetary system were formed either at the same time or in a related series of events. Both Hoyle and Cameron attempt to show that the formation of a solar nebula must be an inevitable consequence of the formation of the sun. However, the details of their suggested processes are greatly different, and the resulting solar nebulae have little in common. Clearly, there is much room for research here. The new chronometric methods resulting from the discovery by J. H. Reynolds of isotopic anomalies in meteoritic xenon may be of great assistance in carrying out such research.

The history of past cosmogonies warns us not to put too much faith in the ideas expressed in this book. But this does not mean that the ideas are not worthwhile. The best way to obtain new ideas is to find weaknesses in old ones. The fact that successful conferences can now be held on the subject of the origin of the solar system indicates that there are now plenty of people who are trying to do just that.

REFERENCES

* In historical order.

1. R. Descartes, "Principia Philosophiae." Amsterdam, 1644.
2. G. L. L. Buffon, "De la formation des planètes." Paris, 1745.
3. I. Kant, "Allgemeine Naturgeschichte und Theorie des Himmels." 1755.
4. P. S. de Laplace, "Exposition du système du Monde." Paris, 1796.
5. A. W. Bickerton, *Trans. New Zealand Inst.* **11**, 125 (1878).
6. T. C. Chamberlin, *Astrophys. J.* **14**, 17 (1901).
7. F. R. Moulton, *Astrophys. J.* **22**, 165 (1905).
8. T. J. J. See, "The Capture Theory of Cosmical Evolution: Researches on the Evolution of the Steller System," Vol. II. Nichols, Lynn, Massachusetts, 1910.
9. K. Birkeland, *Compt. rend. acad. sci.* **155**, 892 (1912).
10. H. Poincaré, "Leçons sur les hypothèses cosmogoniques." Hermann, Paris, 1913.
11. S. Arrhenius, "Das Werden der Welten." Leipzig, 1913.
12. H. Jeffreys, *Monthly Notices Roy. Astron. Soc.* **77**, 84 (1916).
13. J. H. Jeans, *Mem. Roy. Astron. Soc.* **62**, 1 (1917).
14. H. Jeffreys, *Monthly Notices Roy. Astron. Soc.* **78**, 424, 1918.
15. J. H. Jeans, "Problems of Cosmogony and Stellar Dynamics." Cambridge Univ. Press, London and New York, 1919.
16. F. Nölke, "Das Problem der Enticklung unseres Planetensystems." Berlin, 1919.
17. H. Jeffreys, "The Earth." Cambridge Univ. Press, London and New York, 1924.
18. T. C. Chamberlin, "The Origin of the Earth." Chicago, 1927.
19. H. P. Berlage, Jr., *Ergänzungsband Gerlands Beitr. Geophys.* **17** (1927).
20. J. H. Jeans, "Astronomy and Cosmogony." Cambridge Univ. Press, London and New York, 1928.
21. H. Jeffreys, *Monthly Notices Roy. Astron. Soc.* **89**, 636 (1929).
22. H. P. Berlage, Jr., *Proc. Koninkl. Ned. Akad. Wetenschap. (Amsterdam)* **33**, 614, 719 (1930).
23. H. P. Berlage, Jr., "Het ontstaan en vergaan der werelden." Amsterdam, 1930.
23a. F. Nölke, "Der Entwicklungsgang unseres Planetensystems." Bonn, 1930.
24. H. P. Berlage, Jr., *Proc. Koninkl. Ned. Akad. Wetenschap. (Amsterdam)* **35**, 553 (1932).
25. H. P. Berlage, Jr., *Proc. Koninkl. Ned. Akad. Wetenschap. (Amsterdam)* **37**, 221 (1934).
26. H. P. Berlage, Jr., *Proc. Koninkl. Ned. Akad. Wetenschap. (Amsterdam)* **38**, 857 (1935).
27. H. N. Russell, "The Solar System and its Origin." Macmillan, New York, 1935.
28. R. A. Lyttleton, *Monthly Notices Roy. Astron. Soc.* **96**, 559 (1936).
29. R. A. Lyttleton, *Monthly Notices Roy. Astron. Soc.* **98**, 536 (1938).
30. R. A. Lyttleton, *Monthly Notices Roy. Astron. Soc.* **98**, 646 (1938).
31. L. Spitzer, *Astrophys. J.* **90**, 675 (1939).
32. H. P. Berlage, Jr., *Proc. Koninkl. Ned. Akad. Wetenschap. (Amsterdam)* **43**, 532, 557 (1940).
33. R. A. Lyttleton, *Monthly Notices Roy. Astron. Soc.* **101**, 216 (1941).
34. R. A. Lyttleton, *Monthly Notices Roy. Astron. Soc.* **101**, 349 (1941).
35. H. Alfvén, *Stockholms Obs. Ann.* **14**, No. 2 (1942).
36. H. Alfvén, *Stockholms Obs. Ann.* **14**, No. 5 (1943).
37. F. Hoyle, *Proc. Cambridge Phil. Soc.* **40**, 256 (1944).

38. C. F. von Weizsäcker, *Z. Astrophys.* **22,** 319 (1944).
39. H. N. Russell, R. S. Dugan, and J. Q. Stewart, "Astronomy," Vol. I. Boston, 1945.
40. F. Hoyle, *Monthly Notices Roy. Astron. Soc.* **105,** 175 (1945).
41. J. M. Burgers, *Proc. Koninkl. Ned. Akad. Wetenschap. (Amsterdam)* **49,** 589 (1946).
42. F. Hoyle, *Monthly Notices Roy. Astron. Soc.* **106,** 406 (1946).
43. H. Alfvén, *Stockholms Obs. Ann.* **14,** No. 9 (1946).
44. C. F. von Weizsäcker, *Naturwissenschaften* **33,** 8 (1946).
45. S. Chandrasekhar, *Revs. Modern Phys.* **18,** 94 (1946).
46. F. L. Whipple, paper read before the American Association for the Advancement of Science, Chicago, December 27, 1947.
47. H. P. Berlage, Jr., *Proc. Koninkl. Ned. Akad. Wetenschap. (Amsterdam)* **51,** 796 (1948).
48. H. P. Berlage, Jr., *Proc. Koninkl. Ned. Akad. Wetenschap. (Amsterdam)* **51,** 965 (1948).
49. F. L. Whipple, *Harvard Obs. Monographs* No. 7 (1948).
50. D. ter Haar, *Kgl. Danske Videnskap. Selskab, Mat.-Fys. Medd.* **25,** 3 (1948).
51. G. P. Kuiper, *Astrophys. J.* **109,** 308 (1949).
52. D. ter Haar, *Astrophys. J.* **111,** 179 (1950).
53. H. C. Urey, *Geochim. et Cosmochim. Acta* **1,** 209 (1951).
54. G. P. Kuiper, *Proc. Natl. Acad. Sci. U. S.* **37,** 1 (1951).
55. G. P. Kuiper, *in* "Astrophysics" (J. A. Hynek, ed.), Chapter 8. McGraw-Hill, New York, 1951.
56. H. C. Urey, "The Planets: Their Origin and Development." Yale Univ. Press, New Haven, Connecticut, 1952.
57. D. ter Haar, *Proc. Roy. Soc. Edinburgh* **64,** 1 (1953).
58. H. Alfvén, "On the Origin of the Solar System." Oxford Univ. Press (Clarendon), London and New York, 1954.
59. O. Schmidt, "A Theory of the Origin of the Earth; Four Lectures." Lawrence & Wishart, London, 1959.

Star Formation

LYMAN SPITZER, JR.

Department of Astrophysical Sciences, Princeton University, Princeton, New Jersey

I. Introduction

An impressive body of information leads strongly to the conclusion that stars are forming and have been formed within the Galaxy during the last ten to one hundred million years. This evidence is of various types. Stars in groups are observed to be receding from one another with velocities which indicate that the associations formed a few million years ago. The high luminosity of these bright early-type stars also shows that these stars are much younger than the universe, with ages of a few million years indicated.

Star formation seems to take place in those regions where gas and dust are present in very appreciable quantities. In those galaxies or in those parts of a galaxy where there is very little interstellar gas, or no observable obscuration due to small particles or dust, there is apparently no star formation; at least in these regions there are very few, if any, very bright stars of high surface temperature.

These three lines of evidence—expansion of star associations, the existence of bright highly luminous stars, and the close connection between these young stars and interstellar gas and dust—provide conclusive evidence that stars are being formed at the present time in our Galaxy and probably in other spiral galaxies.

How nature manages to form stars is obviously a question of very great physical interest. We do not have the complete answer to this question but we can analyze the possibilities and show what the basic problems are.

In this discussion I shall limit myself to those stars for which we have definite information about their densities, pressures and temperatures and

39

similar information about the surrounding interstellar matter. The present paper, therefore, will be limited to the formation of the relatively young stars of Baade's population type I. The old stars of population type II, which are found throughout the Galaxy, were presumably formed some 5×10^9 years ago. Information on physical conditions in a galaxy or proto-galaxy at so remote a time is entirely speculative; for example, the ratio of grains to gas and of oxygen to hydrogen, the intensity of cosmic rays, and even the ratio of gravitational to electrostatic forces at this early time are all quite uncertain. Hence we shall consider here only the young stars which are forming currently in spiral arms.

II. Environment of Star Formation

What are the physical conditions of the interstellar material from which stars are presently forming? This is a subject where our information is rather limited, but some definite knowledge is available.

We are fairly certain that a large amount of neutral hydrogen is dis-tributed throughout the galactic plane, with a temperature in the general neighborhood of 100°K. The mean density of this hydrogen is about one atom per cm^3 within a spiral arm. It is believed that the density within clouds of gas is substantially higher than this, in the neighborhood of 10 to 10^2 hydrogen atoms per cm^3. In exceptionally dense and bright regions, such as the rather unusual Orion nebula, the densities are as high as 10^3 electrons per cm^3. As far as we know such very high densities are rather exceptional and most of the interstellar clouds have densities in the neigh-borhood of ten to a hundred atoms per cm^3, with these densities extending over regions of many parsecs.

We know that there is some ionization of these clouds; the electron den-sity is usually assumed to be about 10^{-4} times the hydrogen density. Lastly, we know that the clouds are all in motion, with three-dimensional velocities averaging about 15 km/sec, but with some velocities as high as 100 km/sec. The presence of such high velocities shows that the distribution of velocities is not Maxwellian.

The major uncertainty at the present time in the physical condition of interstellar material is the strength and topography of the magnetic field in space. This is a very lively research topic. In recent years the most fashionable view has been that there is a field of 2×10^{-5} gauss parallel to the spiral arms; a number of lines of evidence suggest this hypothesis. There has also been an alternative point of view that the field is substantially weaker, say of the order of 10^{-6} gauss, in which case the lines of force are not uniform and parallel to the axis of the spiral arms but are tangled and jumbled. One then has an ellipsoidal distribution of magnetic field vectors, with the major axis of this distribution parallel to the spiral arms. The low fields would be dominated by the motions of the gas, while the high field would in itself dominate these motions.

Regardless of which view is accepted, one must make protective hypotheses, which complicate the picture, but are needed to explain away a number of observations. In the case of the very low field it is difficult to attribute the radio noise from the Galaxy to synchrotron radiation emitted by energetic electrons in the galactic magnetic field, if the observations of energetic electrons in cosmic rays reaching the earth are accepted as typical of the Galaxy generally. On the other hand if one believes in the high field, then one must explain away the recent 21-cm observations which have failed to find so high a field in the few clouds that have been examined. As shown below, one is also in some difficulty with star formation if the magnetic field is as high as 2×10^{-5} gauss.

III. Stages in Star Formation

Let me briefly outline an idealized picture by which we might imagine that stars are formed. Several stages in the formation of a star will first be listed, and then discussed in more detail. It should be emphasized that all this discussion is quite tentative and serves primarily to point out some of the problems involved.

The *first stage* is the formation of an interstellar cloud, and its growth or compression or modification in some way so that it reaches gravitational instability and starts contracting.

The *second stage* in this process, which was analyzed a number of years ago by Hoyle, is the collapse and fragmentation of the cloud. There is observational evidence that star formation which goes on at the present time occurs mostly in large groups. We cannot exclude the possibility that individual stars are formed separately from individual clouds, but most of the young stars were apparently formed in groups of perhaps several hundred solar masses. This second stage is one in which the cloud collapses and at the same time condenses throughout its body into smaller units which then form a collapsing protocluster of protostars.

The *third stage* begins when fragmentation ceases. This stage is reached when the opacity of the cloud becomes sufficiently high so that the material builds up its temperature to the point where an isothermal collapse no longer occurs. When the star becomes opaque and the central temperature builds up to the value computed from the virial theorem, fragmentation ceases and Helmholtz contraction of each individual protostar begins.

The *fourth stage*, analyzed recently by Cameron, is a gravitational collapse of the protostar resulting from the dissociation and ionization of hydrogen. This reduces the adiabatic exponent γ below $4/3$ throughout the body of the protostar. Fragmentation of the protostar into smaller units may possibly resume during this fourth stage.

The *fifth stage* essentially starts when the mean temperature of a protostar reaches about 100,000°K so that all the hydrogen and all the helium are ionized, and γ increases above $4/3$. In the case of the sun this would correspond to a radius of about a hundred times its present radius, or roughly the radius of the earth's orbit. During this fifth stage the protostar undergoes a second Helmholtz contraction until nuclear energy generation begins. This stage has been considered part of stellar evolution proper and will not be discussed here.

These different stages form the basis for much of the theoretical work that has been published about star formation. As one indication of the many uncertainties in star formation theory it should be noted that possibly some of these stages do not even arise during the actual process of star birth.

IV. Stage One—Formation of Interstellar Clouds

In one sense the study of cloud formation is not necessary in a theory of star formation because we know observationally that clouds exist. However, it is interesting to examine the processes that are available to form aggregations of matter. There are a number of instabilities present in a homogeneous medium of interstellar density subject to the known radiation field. One of these is thermal instability, which a number of people have analyzed.

Under certain conditions, a small temperature fluctuation can lead to either strong cooling or strong heating. If the gain of kinetic energy from the interstellar radiation field rises as the temperature rises, or, more likely, if the energy loss from inelastic collisions falls off sufficiently sharply as the temperature rises, then temperature instability results. Field has analyzed this problem and shown that much of the formation of interstellar clouds might be due to this process.

Another related process which might accentuate the phenomenon of instability is the contraction of grains toward each other due to the force exerted by radiation pressure. In a homogeneous medium the grains will tend to cluster together, and the cooling effect of the grains will then tend to cool down the aggregations of gas in which the grains are somewhat concentrated. The grains are not likely to concentrate to a very large extent;

specifically, the ratio of grains to gas is not likely to go up to a very high value because the rate of diffusion goes down when the clouds contract. But the grains might well be drawn from considerable regions of the interstellar gas between clouds, through action of this mechanism, leaving these intercloud regions free to get hot.

These two instabilities can produce appreciable temperature differences within the gas and can lead to substantial density differences because of the tendency of interstellar material to reach pressure equilibrium.

One can also assume that the clouds have been formed by dynamic processes. We know that interstellar material sometimes has large velocities, and we think we know something about how the velocities might be produced. One way could be by explosions of supernovae. Another way might be through the process of star formation itself, for when a star is born it heats up the gas for many parsecs around and shoots it out. In either case these high velocities would be expected to produce density differences within the interstellar gas. When streams of gas collide at supersonic velocities, for example, considerable compression of the gas is to be expected. Evidently there is a variety of processes that can be invoked to account for the inhomogeneous or cloudy character of the interstellar gas.

V. Start of Second Stage—Instability of Protostar

We consider now the conditions under which a cloud will be unstable. The problem in the Galaxy is that we have a mass of gas which is in equilibrium already. It is not an infinite homogeneous gas, as considered in the classical analysis by Jeans, but a finite mass in gravitational equilibrium. Under what conditions can subcondensations of the major condensation become unstable? This problem has been analyzed in considerable detail by a number of authors—Ebert, McCrae, Bonner, and others; we review here the mechanisms involved.

These authors reason that somewhere in the galactic disk there is a cloud which for some reason is at a lower temperature than the surrounding medium, whose pressure has some finite value. We thus have a sphere in equilibrium under an external pressure. Since we assume that the opacity of the sphere is sufficiently low for radiation to pass through it, the whole sphere is isothermal. We further assume that within the sphere the temperature is approximately a hundred degrees, with the hydrogen essentially neutral. Outside the sphere the hydrogen is ionized and at a temperature of about 10,000°K. Since the pressure, at least near the surface, is taken to be the same inside and outside, the large difference in temperature between the sphere and its surroundings produces a substantial difference in density.

In a vacuum an isothermal sphere must have an infinite mass, but in a region of constant pressure the sphere can have a finite mass. As the external pressure increases, the radius, R, of the sphere decreases, if the mass, M, and the internal temperature both are constant. One finds that there is a maximum external pressure which this globule can support, and for M/R^2 above some critical value this globule will become unstable. If the external pressure is gradually increased, the globule becomes more and more centrally condensed until finally it reaches the critical point above which instability sets in. From the values for the mass distribution and pressure distribution in an isothermal sphere, tabulated by Chandrasekhar and Wares, one finds that this critical value is

$$M/R^2 = 5.0(P/G)^{1/2} \tag{1}$$

where P is the external pressure and G the gravitational constant. Using reasonable values for P we obtain 7.6×10^{-3} gm/cm^2 for M/R^2. Since M/R^2 is the material in a column 1 cm^2 in cross section extending outward from the center of the protostar, this quantity is evidently related to the total optical thickness of the cloud. If the material is assumed to have the same opacity per gram as interstellar matter generally, a value of 7.6×10^{-3} gm/cm^2 for M/R^2 corresponds to an extinction of 1.5 magnitudes. If R is set equal to 20 pc this critical condition corresponds to a hydrogen density of about 20 per cm^3 and to a mass of 1.6×10^4 $M_\odot$. The existence of cloud complexes of roughly this size was first pointed out by Greenstein, who gave a list of such cloud complexes in various parts of the sky. Thus if one assumes that there is no magnetic field, one comes out with the result that many of the observed cloud complexes are about on the verge of gravitational instability.

This analysis neglects internal motions in the cloud. This neglect appears to be justified by recent 21-cm results, which for the denser clouds indicate internal motions of about 1.5 km/sec, roughly equal to the thermal motions of hydrogen at 100°. If one added a little turbulence, the critical mass would come up somewhat and only the densest cloud complexes would be about to contract.

Magnetic Field Intensity

This picture changes appreciably if a strong magnetic field is assumed to be present. If we take equation (1) rather blindly and say we have a magnetic field of 2×10^{-5} gauss, the pressure is increased by about a factor of 100. Hence for a cloud that is just unstable M/R^2 will be ten times as great, corresponding to a total extinction of 15 magnitudes. One can scarcely say that there are many such large clouds around, because a cloud of this opacity extending over 20 parsecs would not have gone unnoticed!

However, equation (1) is not really applicable if a strong magnetic field is present, since the internal pressure is no longer proportional to the density as the cloud contracts. If three-dimensional contraction is assumed, the magnetic field varies inversely as $1/R^2$, since the flux through the protocluster must remain constant; the density, on the other hand, goes as $1/R^3$. On this basis the magnetic field varies as $n^{2/3}$, and the magnetic pressure varies as $n^{4/3}$. If we forget about the two-dimensional nature of the magnetic field, and ask what is the equilibrium of a star with a strong magnetic field, we find it corresponds to a polytrope with $n = 3$, or $\gamma = 4/3$.

If such a configuration is in equilibrium in one condition, it will still be in equilibrium if it is compressed. It will be in a sort of neutral equilibrium, with the radius indeterminate. Thus if a large magnetic field is responsible for the pressure, a cloud cannot become unstable as a result of compression.

In the presence of a strong magnetic field the criterion for instability yields a limit on the mass, and there is a critical mass M_c which is just unstable. If the gas pressure is ignored, the magnetic energy density is about equal to the gravitational energy per cm³ at this critical mass and we have, approximately,

$$M_c \approx B^3/16(2G)^{3/2}\rho^2 \qquad (2)$$

If we take B equal to 2×10^{-5} gauss and set ρ equal to 3×10^{-23} gm/cm³, corresponding to 20 hydrogen atoms per cm³, we find that this critical mass is of the order of 10^7 solar masses.

If one assumes that in the original cloud the magnetic field, B, was less by a factor of 10, then the critical mass reduces by a factor of 10^3 because M is proportional to B^3. So, if a weak field is assumed, the critical mass is in the region of 10^4 solar masses, which is in rough agreement with the observed cloud complexes.

We conclude that it is difficult to visualize a magnetic field as great as 10^{-5} gauss in the bulk of the interstellar cloud if star formation is to take place by contraction of the cloud. But if we reduce the magnetic field to 2×10^{-6} gauss, there is no problem with the initial instability.

VI. Development of Second Stage—Collapse and Fragmentation

We turn now to a consideration of what happens as the second stage develops, and as the protocluster collapses. This process is very difficult to analyze in detail, and most of the present discussion will be devoted to the role of the magnetic field during this stage.

Throughout this section we shall consider a protocluster with a mass of $10^3 M_\odot$. Physical parameters characterizing this collapsing cloud in various stages of its collapse are given in Table I. The table extends up to densities of about 10^{10} H atoms per cm^3, since this is probably about the density at which the opacity becomes sufficiently large to stop the collapse.

In columns five and six of Table I are listed v_f, the velocity of free fall, and t_f, the time required for the cloud to collapse to its center. Evidently for uniform radial contraction of a self-gravitating sphere with zero internal pressure, we have

$$v_f{}^2 = GM/R \qquad (3)$$

while

$$t_f = 2R/3v_f \qquad (4)$$

It is not clear how relevant these computed values are, since it is likely that the initial globule would not be quiescent, and turbulent motions would unquestionably increase the time required for the globule to collapse. In the presence of turbulence, but in the absence of a magnetic field or net rotation, the cloud will tend to oscillate. As the turbulent elements collide and dissipate their relative motion the cloud will contract further. How much the time of contraction might exceed the computed times of free fall is rather difficult to say, but an increase by a factor of about five might be a reasonable expectation.

If the globule possesses angular momentum initially, then it will obviously not contract to its center unless there is some mechanism for disposing of the angular momentum. In the past, turbulence has been invoked for carrying away the angular momentum of a protostar or protocluster. More rerecently, this function has been attributed to the magnetic field. It seems clear that if the magnetic lines of force in a collapsing gas cloud are connected to the surrounding gas, far from the cloud, the cloud rotation must be damped.

The central problem of the collapse process is what happens to the magnetic field during this stage. Quite apart from the effect of this field on rotation, the fragmentation of the protocluster into fragments of smaller mass is strongly influenced by the magnetic field. If B is zero or very small, then, as the density increases, smaller and smaller masses become unstable, and as time goes on the cloud fragments into smaller and smaller masses.

When a relatively strong magnetic field is added, this process must stop. As the cloud contracts, the gas pressure rises only in direct proportion to the density, because the temperature is assumed constant. However, the magnetic pressure increases as $\rho^{4/3}$, and increases relative to the gas pressure as ρ increases. When the two pressures are equal the critical mass is given by equation (2) and is then constant with further contraction, since B^3/ρ^2 is constant.

TABLE I

Interstellar Cloud Parameters

R (pc)	n_H (cm^{-3})	M/R^2 (gm/cm^2)	B (gauss)	v_f (km/sec)	t_f (years)	v_d (km/sec)	t_{eq} (years)	$t_{B\theta}$ (years)
20	20	8×10^{-3}	2×10^{-6}	1.8	10^7	8×10^{-5}	2×10^7	8×10^6
2	2×10^4	0.8	2×10^{-4}	5.7	3×10^5	0.008	2×10^4	8×10^4
0.2	2×10^7	80	2×10^{-2}	18	10^4	0.8	20	8×10^2
0.02	2×10^{10}	8×10^3	2	57	300	11	.02	8

R = radius
n_H = number of hydrogen atoms
M = mass
B = magnetic field strength
t_f = time of free fall
v_f = velocity of free fall

v_d = velocity of lines of force and charged particles
through the neutral gas
t_{eq} = time required for ion density to decrease by a
factor of $1/e$
$t_{B\theta}$ = decay time for the lowest mode dipole field

If, as in Table I, we assume a magnetic field of 2×10^{-6} gauss at the initial phase, then it is concievable that the mass might fragment once into masses of perhaps a half or a third of the original mass. But after that fragmentation would cease and the magnetic field would then increase by a factor of 10^2 for each successive increase of ρ by 10^3.

If we wish to assume formation of stars of solar mass out of this aggregate, we must somehow dispose of the magnetic field. There are two ways of doing this. One can, as in the approach taken by Cameron, assume that the magnetic field is already out of the cloud and that the ratio of B to $n^{2/3}$ in the initial cloud is less by several orders of magnitude than the upper limits that we have given. We may be driven to this assumption if we cannot get rid of the magnetic field in any other way. The second way is to separate the magnetic field from the gas by ambipolar diffusion during the collapse.

A. Separation of Magnetic Field and Cloud

This subject was analyzed sometime ago in a paper by Mestel and myself. It was pointed out that as a cloud collapsed the electron density would fall sharply because the ionizing radiation is cut off. At a sufficiently low density of charged particles the lines of force become uncoupled from the neutral gas, and move out of the cloud. We computed a velocity of the lines of force through the gas about equal to several kilometers per second.

The basic physical picture is this: a collapsing protostar has pulled in the lines of force, and as a result of the magnetic stresses the lines of force tend to pull out, taking the electrons and positive ions along with them. The force pulling the lines of force out is roughly given by $B^2/8\pi R$ where R is the cloud radius. This force must be balanced by collisions between the ions which are "glued" to the lines of force and the neutral atoms which are ignorant of the fact that any magnetic field is there. These collisions produce an exchange of momentum between the ions and the neutral atoms, which just counterbalances the magnetic stress. Hence we obtain

$$B^2/8\pi R = n_i n_n \overline{\sigma v} m_n v_d \tag{5}$$

The collision rate is the product of the ion density, n_i, the neutral density, n_n, the cross section, σ, and v, the relative random velocity of ions and neutral atoms; as usual, σv is averaged over a Maxwellian distribution. The exchange of momentum per collision equals the mass m_m of a neutral atom multiplied by the drift velocity, v_d, of the lines of force and the ions through the gas. Since the ions and electrons are moving at the same rate through the gas, this process is an example of ambipolar diffusion. Equation (5) then determines the rate at which the lines of force drift outwards through the neutral gas. It is clear that as we make n_i smaller and smaller and smaller, v_d gets bigger and bigger and bigger.

In our paper Mestel and I applied this result to a protocluster in which the hydrogen density was of the order of 10^4; i.e., the cloud radius had fallen by a factor of 10, with the density increasing by a factor of 1000. For those conditions the drift velocity was roughly given by $10^3/n_i$ cm/sec. If n_i is less than 10^{-2}, the drift velocity can be several kilometers per second, and appreciable separation of the magnetic field from the gas can occur.

Why should the electron density be so low? Our argument was that there was no ionizing radiation, and the ions would disappear quite rapidly by colliding with the grains. If we assume that every positive ion striking a grain either sticks or comes off as a neutral, the change of n_i with time is given by

$$dn_i/dt = -n_i n_g \sigma v \equiv -n_i/t_{eg} \tag{6}$$

The time required for the positive ion density to fall by $1/e$ by colliding with the grains is indicated by t_{eg} in Table I. In this computation $n_g \sigma_g/n_H$ is set equal to 5×10^{-22} cm^2, its value for interstellar matter generally, as indicated by a mean extinction of 1.6 mag/kpc and a mean hydrogen density of 1 atom/cm^3. Evidently t_{eg} falls appreciably below t_f early in the collapse. Hence the assumption that the ions disappear rapidly by colliding with the grains would appear to be a good one.

Since our work on this problem was published, two things have happened. In the first place, Osterbrock has analyzed the collision cross section in some detail and has shown for the low relative velocities that we are talking about, σ is not equal to 10^{-16} cm^2, the value that we assumed, but 10^{-14}, two orders of magnitude higher. This change reduces v_d down to $10/n_i$ for the protocluster which we considered. So now we must make n_i even smaller by a factor of 100 if appreciable separation of magnetic field and cloud is to occur. This is perhaps not too difficult if there is really no ionizing radiation.

In the second place, however, a number of astronomers have pointed out in the last few years, in Japan and in this country, that if one extrapolates the number of cosmic rays from the ten billion volt level, where we are really sure of it, down to energies of about a billion volts, one obtains a substantial increase in the number of ion pairs produced by cosmic rays.

On the basis of this extrapolation the rate of ionization of the interstellar gas by cosmic rays is increased by a factor of ten above the values that we took a number of years ago. The electron density, or the ion density now becomes 0.006 per cubic centimeter. This value, which is independent of the gas density, is computed for $n_g \sigma_g/n_H$ again set equal to 5×10^{-22} cm^2, typical of interstellar material generally. The constancy of n_i as n_n changes results from the assumption that ionization of hydrogen by cosmic rays is proportional to n_n, while the recombination rate is proportional to n_g. Hence if the ratio of n_n to n_g is constant, then n_i is also constant. With this value of n_i, the diffusion velocity, v_d, is now only 800 cm/sec, the value given in Table I for R equal to 2 pc. The other values of v_d in Table I are also computed for this same low value if n_i; when v_d exceeds the thermal velocity of the neutral atoms, v is replaced by v_d in equation (6).

Evidently on the basis of these new assumptions it is very difficult to separate the magnetic field from the gas at an early stage in the contraction of the protostar.

One possible escape from this dilemma is provided by the absorption of cosmic rays in the cloud. The amount of material required to absorb cosmic rays is 50 gm/cm^2. From Table I we see that when the radius of the proto-cluster has fallen to 0.2 pc the amount of material along a line to the cloud center is 80 gm/cm^2; since the particles will be spiraling around the lines of force, the effective value is somewhat greater. At this stage the cosmic rays that are maintaining the ion density begin to be absorbed. If n_i falls by one or two orders of magnitude, v_d will be correspondingly increased, and especially if the effective value of v_f is reduced by turbulence, rotation or similar effects, appreciable separation of the magnetic field and the gas may occur.

I would conclude from this discussion of ambipolar diffusion that even with these new higher cross sections, we have a reasonable chance of getting the electron densities low enough so that the magnetic field will be sharply reduced during the later stages of the collapse, permitting fragmentation to proceed.

B. Maintenance of Magnetic Field by Grains

Although invoking the grains has proved very helpful in reducing n_i, we must now watch out that the grains themselves do not provide charged carriers that will maintain the current. In fact, it is likely that the grains will be charged; as the ions and electrons collect on the grains, it is rather unlikely that each grain will be neutral. After most of the ions and electrons have collected on the grains, the probability is that half the grains will be positive and half negative.

We shall now analyze the effect that this additional source of conductivity will have in maintaining the magnetic field. The charged grains behave quite differently from the positive ions. The positive ions (and electrons) spiral around the lines of magnetic force, with relatively infrequent collisions. Hence, generally, they drift with the lines of force. The grains, on the other hand, have a mobility which is very much less, and their gyration time in the magnetic field is very much longer; as a result to a first approximation they move parallel to the electric field, and do not follow the lines of force. Thus, we have essentially the problem of the decay time of a magnetic field with classical conductivity. One can analyze this problem and compute the decay time for the magnetic field with the conventional number of grains, assuming that half of them are positive and half of them are negative. If a grain with a radius of 3×10^{-5} cm has a net charge of one electron, the mean potential at the surface is 5×10^{-3} volts; at a temperature of $50°K$, another electron will have just about enough energy to surmount the potential barrier and strike the surface of the grain. Hence the grains should have a net charge about equal to one electron. The familiar approximate formula for the decay of the lowest magnetic mode in a spherical conducting magnet of radius R and of uniform conductivity, σ, is

$$t_B = 4R^2\sigma/\pi \tag{7}$$

The conductivity due to grains is limited by collisions between grains and gas, and is given by

$$\sigma = n_g Z_g^2 e^2/\pi a^2 c^2 n_H m_H v_H \tag{8}$$

where $Z_g e$ is the net charge on a grain, and v_H is the mean thermal velocity of the hydrogen atoms. Hence we obtain for t_{Bg}, the magnetic decay time in the presence of grains,

$$t_{Bg} = 4R^2 n_g Z_g^2 e^2/\pi^2 a^2 n_H m_H v_H c^2 \tag{9}$$

Values of t_{Bg} for Z_g^2 equal to one are given in Table I, computed on the assumption that all the grains have a radius of 3×10^{-5} cm, with n_g/n_H equal to 1.7×10^{-13}. For any higher mode the times will be shorter. This time is somewhat shorter than the values of t_f, the time of free fall. On the other hand grains of smaller a are much more effective in maintaining the magnetic field. If n_g has the same value for grains of radius 10^{-5} cm as we have assumed for the larger grains, t_{Bg} is increased by an order of magnitude. In this case the magnetic field will decay appreciably only if the collapse is delayed by turbulence or other effects; we have already seen such a delay is rather likely. Evidently a more detailed study, taking into account the distribution of grain radii and the dynamics of the collapse, would be required for conclusive results on this topic.

The main conclusion of this discussion on the second stage is that while we cannot be certain that the magnetic field will be driven out of the protocluster and that fragmentation will occur, these results seem at least possible.

VII. State Three—Helmholtz Contraction of Protostar

Now let us consider when stage three begins. It is possible that stage four begins directly and that stage three does not appear. The condition for stage three to begin is that leakage of radiation is less rapid than the rate at which energy is being released by the compression of the gas. Alternatively stage three begins when the computed velocity of the Helmholtz contraction is less than the velocity of free fall. The rate at which radiation leaks out is proportional to the radiation pressure, P_R, times the velocity of light divided by τ, the optical thickness from the surface down to the center of the protostar. The rate at which the energy is released in Helmholtz contraction is proportional to the velocity of free fall times the gas pressure, P_G. So the condition in which opacity raises the central temperature and keeps it at its equilibrium at the value given by the virial theorem is very roughly that

$$\tau > \frac{Ct_f}{R}\frac{P_R}{P_G} \tag{10}$$

For a protocluster with a mass of $10^3 M_\odot$ the ratio of the radiation to gas pressure in equilibrium, which may be obtained approximately from Eddington's quartic equation, is of the order of unity or greater. From relation (10) we see that the optical thickness of the cloud in infrared radiation must be large compared with 10^5.

J. Gaustad at Princeton has been studying the opacity of a contracting protostar. Both grains and molecules must be considered. While the contribution of the grains to the opacity can be computed without great difficulty, the corresponding computation for molecules is a difficult problem. The familiar absorption by molecular bands, which are responsible for the very large opacity in planetary atmospheres, is probably relatively unimportant in an interstellar gas cloud; the densities are so much less that pressure broadening is very much less. As a result the molecular lines, instead of being broad and overlapping and producing a continuous absorption, produce isolated lines which do not contribute much to the Rosseland mean opacity. The radiation leaks out between the lines.

One must analyze also the true continuous opacity produced by molecules. One must consider those molecules which are excited, and which can then be dissociated with the absorption of very small amounts of energy. This is a subject which has apparently not been analyzed previously in detail. Preliminary results from Gaustad's work indicate that the continuous opacity due to molecules under these very low pressure conditions is not likely to be as important as the effect of the grains.

VIII. Stage Four—Second Collapse

There is some uncertainty as to the temperature at the beginning of the third stage. If the material has fragmented into objects with about the mass of the sun, the temperature may be somewhat less than that required to dissociate the hydrogen molecules. The individual fragments will then remain in the third stage for a while. In this case the value of the opacity will determine the length of time in which stage three persists. But ultimately the temperature will rise to about 1500 or 2000°K; the dissociation of hydrogen will lower γ in the star to less than 4/3, and the material will collapse again.

One has then the interesting problem of whether or not fragmentation will resume during this phase and whether an object of solar mass will condense into smaller fragments during the collapse stage. This depends in large part, of course, on how low the magnetic field has been reduced by the time this process starts, because when the temperature is high enough to ionize most of the atoms, the magnetic field becomes "frozen" in the gas.

While the discussion of these successive stages of star formation has been somewhat tentative and inconclusive, the final stage is not quite so speculative since the phenomena become simpler when the material becomes hotter and fully ionized, when fast dynamical processes come to an end, and when spherical symmetry becomes assured.

Contraction of the Sun toward the Main Sequence

A. G. W. CAMERON

Institute for Space Studies, Goddard Space Flight Center, National Aeronautics and Space Administration, New York

(after M. SCHWARZSCHILD)

This chapter has been prepared by A. G. W. Cameron, based upon the remarks of Martin Scwarzschild at the conference, together with some additional material.

Lyman Spitzer has brought stars through their contraction from the interstellar medium, and has left them at a stage where they are undergoing a final Kelvin-Helmholtz contraction toward the main sequence. We shall be interested in the behavior of the sun during this contraction phase, when its radius is about ten times the present one.

When considering the influence of this solar contraction phase on the formation of the planetary system, we are not interested in the deep interior of the sun as such, but rather in the surface characteristics. This means that we are primarily interested in the luminosity of the sun during that contraction phase, and to a lesser extent in the values of the surface temperature. We are also interested in the possibility that the sun may lose mass during its contraction period.

Let us start by reviewing what until recently was the accepted picture of early solar evolution. Figure 1 shows a schematic sketch of the Hertzsprung–Russell diagram. The line AB marks the main sequence. The present position of the sun in this diagram is at the cross marked C'. According to old calculations by Henyey, Lelevier, and Levee, during the contraction phase of the sun the evolutionary track runs from D to E, and then when nuclear energy generation starts at the center, the track turns down to E to C.

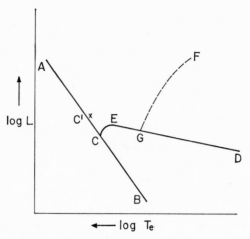

FIG. 1. The Hertzsprung-Russell diagram.

Recent calculations by Brownlee and Cox tend to confirm the general nature of this curve, although of course there are many differences in detail.

It may be noted that the solar luminosity does not change greatly during the course of these calculations. This is a simple consequence of the physics of stellar interiors that was put into the calculations. In order to have hydrostatic equilibrium in the central regions of the star, there must be a certain value for the central temperature that cannot vary over very wide limits, and for the simple conditions that we are considering here this central temperature is essentially fixed by the radius of the model. There will be an average temperature gradient that necessarily accompanies the establishment of a certain central temperature, and this radiative gradient will determine the flow of energy through the star. This picture will hold with only minor variations regardless of whether the energy generation comes from nuclear sources or from gravitational contraction.

The calculations of Henyey, Lelevier, and Levee, and also those of Brownlee and Cox were based upon the premise that the bulk of the contracting sun was in radiative equilibrium. Henyey, Lelevier, and Levee had no surface convection zone at all, and Brownlee and Cox only a rather small one. As long as the great bulk of the sun is in radiative equilibrium, then the rate at which energy flows down the temperature gradient in the interior cannot greatly change, and hence it is not surprising that the calculations did not lead to a very great change in the luminosity of the contracting sun.

Recently Hayashi has pointed out that these older calculations have completely failed to use the right surface boundary conditions for the sun. He has suggested that the sun should have been fully convective in its early contracting phase, and this shou.d have a tremendous influence upon its early luminosity. The convective transport of energy is an extremely efficient process, so that the only limitation upon the rate at which energy can flow through the interior is the rate at which it can be radiated from the surface layers. Thus as one increases the surface area of the sun, one increases the rate at which energy can be radiated away from the surface, and hence increases the luminosity. Thus Hayashi was led to the prediction that the sun would cover only the later part of the evolutionary track from D to E. Instead of traversing the earlier part of this track, the sun would descend on the line about as drawn from F to G. The subsequent evolution would take the traditional route from G to E to C. We shall discuss these ideas of Hayashi in more detail later.

We are now faced with a choice between a high luminosity path and a low luminosity path for the contracting sun. One wonders if it is possible to make an observational choice between these two possibilities. Indeed, we are strongly advised to pick the high luminosity track if we examine Walker's observational Hertzsprung–Russell diagrams of young clusters of stars, many of which are still contracting and approaching the main sequence.

Figure 2 shows a schematic Hertzsprung-Russell diagram of such a young cluster. The diagonal line denotes the usual position of the main sequence. The crosses mark positions in which stars can be observed; actually many more stars are observed with low luminosities than with high, but the

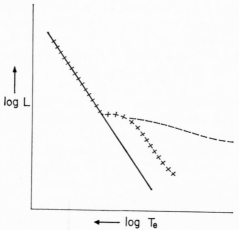

FIG. 2. Schwarzschild origin of solar system.

density of crosses on the diagram has not been increased to suggest this fact.

For quite some time it has been very difficult to understand how the stars could reach their present positions in such a diagram. The greater the mass of the star, the greater is its luminosity and the faster it reaches the main sequence. Indeed, we see that the more massive stars have all reached the main sequence in this cluster. Less massive stars have not yet had time to reach the main sequence. But it is difficult to see how so many of the stars of low mass can have come so close to the main sequence. If they had followed low luminosity tracks, then one should expect to see the stars lying at positions more or less along the broken line shown in Figure 2. This corresponds to the old calculated evolutionary tracks of Henyey, Lelevier, and Levee. How are we to understand that the stars of smaller mass have gotten so much closer to the main sequence than indicated by the broken line?

It should also be noted that the T Tauri stars observed by Herbig lie in this difficult region. These stars show spectral peculiarities that seem to be consistently associated with young clusters, and their total bolometric luminosity seems to be very low. Thus there seems to be no possibility that the observational diagrams are in error, or that these low mass stars lying to the right of the main sequence are really faint red giants that lie far beyond the cluster.

Perhaps somebody would like to formulate a rather strange explanation in which stars of small mass would be the first ones to be formed in a cluster, and stars of large mass would be formed at the very end of the process. This is indeed a very peculiar assumption, since it requires that we have a long period of time during which small mass stars are slowly formed, and then shorter and shorter periods of time for the more massive stars until all the most massive stars are formed in the last 1% or less of the interval. This seems to be a rather unlikely process.

There seems to be no way out of this situation but to assume that the low mass stars in young clusters once had a much greater luminosity, and hence they were able to arrive at their present evolutionary places in the Hertzsprung–Russell diagram in a time much shorter than allowed by the older calculations. Some time ago Lyman Spitzer suggested that the reason these stars had a larger luminosity was that they were probably more massive, and they arrived at their present position as a result of losing mass during their contraction phases.

According to the ordinary mass-luminosity law, in this range the luminosity increases as the third or fourth power of the mass. Hence one could increase the luminosity by some two orders of magnitude if the mass were to increase by a factor of three or so.

Hence one of the possibilities that must be kept in mind is that a typical star goes through all of the contraction phases described by Lyman Spitzer with a mass much greater than that with which it arrives at the main sequence. In the late stages of its contraction it may lose 50 to 70% of its mass. We have not the slightest idea about the mechanisms responsible for this mass loss, except that it would not be surprising to have rotational instability. We often see stars in which this is the situation. Herbig observes very rapid rates of mass loss from his T Tauri stars. This would obviously be a very important event in the early history of the solar system.

The other possibility is to accept the suggestion of Hayashi that stars of solar mass were once much more luminous than they now are. If stars traverse something like the evolutionary track *FG* of Fig. 1, then they would certainly arrive at positions about where they are observed in young clusters within the necessary amount of time. Thus the Hertzsprung-Russell diagrams for young clusters are certainly qualitatively consistent with Hayashi's suggestion.

As was stated earlier, the basis for Hayashi's suggestion of convective stellar models is his conclusion that the older calculations did not contain the right boundary condition in the photosphere of the sun. He based this conclusion on the arguments that Hoyle and Schwarzschild had earlier used to determine that the models of stars in advanced stages of evolution —the red giant stage—should have deep convection zones. The argument is essentially the following. If one takes a star in radiative equilibrium, and increases the radius indefinitely, then the density of material at the surface rapidly decreases. In constructing such models, it was once assumed that the temperature and pressure at the surface were zero. However, it is soon discovered that such a set of conditions is very unsuitable for stars in the red giant phase, since it leads to impossibly large envelopes. One has to choose realistic values for the pressure and temperature in the surface layers. What do we mean by the surface layers? We mean the region of about one optical depth in the photosphere, where the light that is radiated in atomic processes has a good chance of escaping through the surface layers. The density of material in this photospheric layer is thus clearly a function of the opacity. If the opacity is very high, then the density can be low, and conversely.

Now, as a stellar radius increases, the surface temperature tends to decrease. But in the range of a few thousand degrees Kelvin, the opacity also decreases as the temperature decreases. Hence either the temperature cannot be allowed to decrease very rapidly, which leads to a high luminosity consistent with Hayashi's predictions, or the density of the photospheric layer must increase rapidly. But an increase in the photospheric density is quite inconsistent with the general expansion of the model, unless the nature of the model itself changes drastically. Evidently nature must strike a balance between these opposing tendencies, and this balance must therefore lead to at most a very slow decline in temperature and density as the surface area of the star increases.

This does indeed lead to the conclusion that the nature of the model must undergo a great change. In order to keep the density in the photospheric layer high, there must be a great change in the rate at which density varies with temperature throughout the interior. This can only be accomplished by introducing a deep outer convection zone. The parameters of the convection zone are entirely determined by the surface photospheric conditions. In the case of a contracting star like the sun, we can expect the convection zone to extend all the way to the center. This leads to the possibility of a rapid transport of heat from the interior, and the slow decline of the surface temperature, taken together with the great increase in area as we go backward up the evolutionary track, leads to a great increase in the luminosity.

Hayashi predicted that the solar luminosity would be larger by a factor of 10 or more as one goes back up the evolutionary track from G toward F. Indeed, he estimated that the evolution time for the sun to arrive at the point F in Fig. 1 should be only about four million years, and that about another four million years would be required for the sun to move from G to the position C on the main sequence. This would therefore lead to an evolution time of the order of eight million years to reach the main sequence.

Previous estimates put this time in the range fifty to a hundred million years. Thus in Hayashi's view the contraction time of the sun is speeded up by one order of magnitude. This can also be expected to have important consequences for the early history of the solar system. Of course, the evolution time becomes very short in the really high luminosity stages that exceed the present luminosity of the sun by a factor of 10 or more.

During the conference Fowler raised the question of whether the sun could pass through a low-luminosity, low-temperature contraction phase before swinging into the high-luminosity, high temperature contraction phase predicted by Hayashi. Hoyle pointed out that a low-luminosity, low-temperature stage might well be possible owing to the high opacity due to molecules and possibly solid particles present at temperatures around 1000° or 1500°K. Schwarzschild commented that such a phase was certainly conceivable, although after a while it must presumably give way to Hayashi's high-luminosity models, since at some stage the surface temperature must reach 3000° or 4000°K, where the luminosity is not very great and where we might expect Hayashi's conclusions to hold.

TABLE I

CHARACTERISTICS OF SOLAR MODELS IN CONTRACTION PHASE (ONE SOLAR MASS, PRELIMINARY RESULTS)[a]

R/R_0	L/L_0	T_e(°K)
1.5	1.7	5370
2	1.6	4550
3	3.5	4530
5	8.8	4430
10	29	4210
20	89	3940
50	344	3500

[a] R/R_0 is radius in solar units, L/L_0 is luminosity in solar units, and T_e is effective surface temperature.

This chapter is closed with the presentation of Table I, which shows the characteristics of some preliminary solar models in the contraction stage subsequently calculated by D. Ezer and A. G. W. Cameron. These models were constructed with particular attention being paid to obtaining the right photospheric boundary condition; they used opacities computed from the Los Alamos subroutines developed for this purpose, and they imposed the condition that the models must be homologously contracting.

It may be seen that Hayashi's predictions are confirmed, and the sun passes through a high luminosity phase. So far the question has not been investigated as to whether there is an alternate solution for surface temperatures around 1000°K with opacity being very high owing to molecules.

The confirmation of Hayashi's predictions for a high-luminosity phase of the contracting evolution of the star of one solar mass should not cause us to forget Spitzer's suggestion that there may be an additional high-luminosity effect due to mass loss. We do not yet have a proper understanding of the mechanism of mass loss from stars, and so we have no assurance that the constant mass evolution indicated by the models of Table I actually represents the path followed by the sun during its contracting phases.

Formation of the Planets

FRED HOYLE*

Saint John's College, Cambridge, England

It is rather certain that the planets and the meteorites were formed about four and one-half billion years ago, and that a few million years still further back there were nuclear reactions. However, there is very little direct evidence as to how far back one must go to reach the stage where the sun itself was formed. But it probably was not much further back than five billion years ago.

There have been estimates that the original planetary material was as much as 10% of the mass of the sun. The argument for this is based on the condensation of the planets under gravitational forces alone. The center of the system is supposed to have some sort of disk of gas moving in Keplerian orbits. If one demands that condensations form in this gas through gravitational forces, then the disruptive tidal action of the sun's gravitational field must be considered. In order that the tidal action of the sun shall not interfere with the gravitational condensation, it is necessary that the gas density in this disk be greater than the Roche limiting density. That is equivalent to stating that the density must exceed the density obtained by distributing the mass of the sun through a sphere with a radius comparable to that of the disk. This result immediately indicates that the fractional amount of planetary material must be on the order of the ratio of the thickness of the disk to its radius, or about 0.1.

However, it is quite possible that the formation of the planets arose not through gravitational forces, but through the condensation of small solids,

---

* The material of this chapter has been prepared by R. Jastrow from a tape recording of Professor Hoyle's talk. The editors take responsibility for any inaccuracies in the presentation of Professor Hoyle's point of view.

or perhaps, in some cases, of liquid objects, directly from the gaseous phase in a process of gradual accumulation. Once that type of picture is assumed, there is no clear evidence for a disk mass as high as 0.1. One arrives at a figure which is a power of 10 lower, or a fractional mass of 0.01 in the disk.

TABLE I

AUGMENTED MASSES OF THE PLANETS

	Jupiter Saturn	Uranus Neptune	Terrestrial planets
Major constituents	H, He (~100%)[a]	CNO (1.5%)[a]	Mg, Si, Fe (0.25%)[a]
Present masses (10^{-5} $M_\odot$)	100	10	1
Multiplier	1	67	400
Augmented masses (10^{-5} $M_\odot$)	100	670	400

[a] Approximate percentage of the mass of the sun.

In order to reach an estimate of the mass originally in the disk, we first list in Table I the present masses of the major groups of planets, together with their probable major constituents. The last line of Table I contains the mass which the present planets would have if their present composition were augmented to make up the solar composition. It is known, for instance, that CNO forms about 1.5% of the mass of the sun. If one has material largely in the form of CNO, a very large quantity of hydrogen and helium would have to be added to make up the ordinary solar material. In fact, if there is 1.5% of CNO in the sun, then one would have to multiply the amount of CNO by a factor 67. And if a 0.25% is taken for magnesium, silicon, and iron, then one would have to multiply by 400 to obtain solar composition.

It is not necessary to add a substantial amount to Jupiter and Saturn, because these are already composed of hydrogen and helium and their present masses are therefore taken arbitrarily as their primitive masses. Of course, one can argue that perhaps more mass was involved in their condensation, and that some of the hydrogen and helium has escaped in some fashion.

On the outskirts of the solar system there must be provision for a very considerable escape of hydrogen and helium if the picture is at all correct, because the densities of Uranus and Neptune indicate there is little hydrogen and helium on these planets. At the orbit of Uranus, where it is a little more difficult to achieve escape than at Neptune, a body in a Keplerian orbit has a speed of about 7 km/sec. The velocity of escape from the solar system to interstellar space is about 10 km/sec. It has to be noted that a molecule of hydrogen going in this orbit does not need in all cases to acquire a thermal velocity over and above the orbital speed of 10 km/sec. If it has a thermal speed of only 3 km/sec in the direction of its orbital motion, that is enough to secure the escape of that molecule if it lies sufficiently near the surface of the gaseous distribution.

With this point in mind, one must consider whether escape occurs with the temperatures and thermal speeds expected in the solar nebula. The temperature of the sun at its present radius is about 6000°K, and the black body temperature therefore is

$$6000°K \times \left[\frac{\text{solar radius}}{\text{Uranus orbit}}\right]^{1/2}$$

or 100°K. At this temperature the thermal speed of molecular hydrogen is ~1 km/sec. From the theory of planetary atmospheres we know that escape occurs in time that are short compared to the age of the solar system, if the mean thermal velocity is one-third of the velocity increment needed for escape (which we have seen is about 3 km/sec). It appears that at least the conditions for escape of hydrogen are satisfied at the boundary of the solar nebula.

How much angular momentum would there be in the system? This can be very easily calculated. One has an augmented mass which is about 2×10^{31} gm. It is circulating mostly in the region of Uranus, so its radius is about 4×10^{14} cm, and it has in general a speed of about 6 km/sec. The total angular momentum is then about 5×10^{51} units.

Suppose that this amount of angular momentum is present in the primitive sun. At what stage will it become rotationally unstable?

One would like to convert the radius of gyration (k) into an actual radius, but here, of course, one has to estimate the degree to which the primitive sun is centrally condensed. Models of the sun suggest that k^2 is equal to about $R^2/10$, where R is the radius of the primitive sun at any particular moment. This equality holds throughout the contraction, provided the stage has been reached where there is no appreciable distortion of the system by angular momentum effects. Then $MR^2\omega \approx 5 \times 10^{52}$ units.

One expects rotational instability to arise when the kinetic energy per gram of material at the equator of the rotating body is of the general order of the gravitational potential energy. That is to say, in order of magnitude, $R^2\omega \approx MG/R$.

One can now simply eliminate ω between these two equations. Knowing the value of the mass of the sun, one can infer the value R, the radius at which instability would be expected to arise. The number which comes out of these equations is $R \sim 4 \times 10^{12}$ cm, which is about the radius of Mercury. It could differ from that by a factor of 2, but to that degree of precision one expects instability to occur when the radius of the primitive sun is equal to the radius of the orbit of Mercury.

The consequence of rotational instability is the formation of a disk in the equatorial plane of the rotating star. This development is rather similar to the ideas of Laplace. His idea was that the sun became rotationally unstable and that it left behind a series of rings which then condensed to form the planets.

The objections to Laplace's ideas are well known. One is that if condensation is begun, making the sun rotationally unstable at the radius corresponding to the orbits of the big planets such as Jupiter and Saturn, it turns out that as the central condensation continues to shrink, an inordinately large mass is put into the disk that is shed. In fact, according to Laplace's ideas, the disk has about half of the total mass, whereas the observed total mass in the system of planets, augmented to approximate cosmic composition, is only 1% of the solar mass.

There is further the very crucial objection that the sun is left spinning at an equatorial speed of a few hundred kilometers a second when it reaches its present stage. It is observed to have a speed of only two kilometers per second.

These are the basic objections to the idea that the process of rotational instability was a simple hydrodynamic one. In some way, the sun must be coupled to the material of the planetary disk by a torque which has the effect of slowing down the sun, not merely to a speed which is stable against rotational forces, but to a speed which is very small compared to the limiting value for stability. The limiting value of the equatorial speed is in the region of 300 km per second, and the sun must be slowed down a hundred times more than that. In some way, the central object which is initially spinning rapidly must be coupled to the material in the disk. That coupling must go on transmitting angular momentum from the inner region to the disk, even after the central object has been rendered quite stable.

It has been suggested that a magnetic field may couple the inner region to the outer region. If such a field exists, it will get twisted, since the variation of the Keplerian angular velocity with increasing orbital radius will cause the outer parts to lag. A very simple calculation shows how much angular momentum can be transferred in this way by a magnetic torque coupling during a time T. Provided the lines of force are systematically twisted, the angular momentum that can be transferred is the product of the magnetic torque couple and the time during which it acts. This quantity is the product of: (1) the force exerted by the magnetic lines per unit area transverse to the solar radial direction, with a magnitude $H^2/8\pi$; (2) the area of the primitive sun, $4\pi R^2$; (3) the distance $\sim R$ through which the couple acts; and (4) the time T. The amount of angular momentum required to be transferred is 5×10^{52}. Thus,

$$H^2 R^3 T \sim 10^{53}$$

If one sets T equal to the Helmholtz contraction time, about 10^{14} seconds, and R is of the order of 4×10^{12} cm, then from this relation we find that a magnetic field H of the order of magnitude of one gauss will be needed. This is a relatively modest requirement for the magnetic field of the contracting sun. The protostars discussed elsewhere in this volume by Spitzer would have a considerably higher magnetic field if their contraction is extrapolated from the point at which he abandoned them.

What are the possibilities for maintaining such a field over long periods of time? This question raises difficulties. It is clear that such a field will eliminate itself unless a layer of ionized gas exists in the disk to hold the field lines extended. Irregularities also could arise that would tend to bite off the magnetic connection between the sun and the disk because of thinning and ohmic losses in the latter.

One might have to use ideas similar to those of Schatzman for re-establishing the magnetic connection: perhaps magnetic fields are carried out in solar particle streams.

The calculations that have been sketched actually imply that the bulk of the gas must move outwards to the orbits of the great planets in order to take up the full amount of angular momentum. The gas in which the field is anchored may begin at the orbit of Mercury, but most of it must extend to Uranus and Neptune to take up the angular momentum that was originally resident in the sun before evaporating from the solar system. One must now ask whether there are any solid objects, accumulated in the gas, which might drop out of the gas during its outward motion, so that the material necessary to form the inner planets can be left behind.

If the vapor of any chemical compound becomes supersaturated within the solar nebula, then that material must condense on any particles that are present. In particular the abundant materials of the magnesium-silicon-iron group have low saturated vapor pressures which are very likely to be exceeded at the modest temperatures we expect to find in the outward-flowing gas of the disk; hence they will almost certainly form solid particles.

But it is not sufficient just to form solid particles in order that the outward-flowing gas can shed solid matter to form the planets. If the particles are fine smoke particles, then the viscous drag of the gas will just carry them along. The solids must be of the order of a meter in diameter in order to drop out from the gas. Hence one supposes that the inner planets have collected from bodies of the order of a meter or so in dimension.

However, it is unlikely that the iron, magnesium, and silicon can condense into objects of metric size. It is much more likely that they will condense into quite smaller micrometeorites. These small particles should have no direct tendency, of themselves, to stick together. However, if ice can condense about them, then it is quite possible that the ice may serve to bind them together when they collide with one another in the gas.

The likelihood of this supposition relates to the discussion by Schwarzschild on the ideas of Hayashi. One can readily show that if the sun had a very high luminosity during its early phases of the contraction toward the main sequence, then water would be unable to condense at distances of the order of one astronomical unit. That is to say, water vapor would not be supersaturated. However, if there is a portion of the early evolutionary track where the luminosity is less than that of the present sun, perhaps for a radius 50, 40, or even 20 times the present radius of the sun, then water would be able to condense in the vicinity of one astronomical unit. It would not matter if the sun became very hot in the latter stages of its contraction, provided the luminosity were sufficiently low in the early stages to allow formation of ice and the accumulation of small bodies from the tiny particles of dust.

If the ice serves to weld the micrometeorites together, then the size of the ultimate condensations will be determined by the collision velocities between the bodies. One can think of collisions between walls of hard ice. It is likely that the size of the object then depends upon the breaking strength of the ice, and upon the relative velocities of the bodies. The related velocities are the crux of the matter, but if one assumes that they are of the order of a few meters per second, then it is likely that pieces of hard ice of metric dimensions will be quite stable against disruption in collisions. However, a piece of hard ice several hundred meters in size would almost certainly splinter. Hence one should expect sizes in the general metric range.

Thus far, the picture has been based merely upon the conservation of angular momentum. If changes take place in a mechanical system with conservation of angular momentum, then in general there is no conservation of kinetic energy. Usually some of the kinetic energy is dissipated into some other form of energy.

The energy required to push the gas of the solar nebula from the vicinity of Mercury to the vicinity of Uranus and Neptune is very much less than the original energy of rotation of the sun, by a factor of the order of 10. Consequently, most of the energy of rotation of the sun must have been dissipated into some other form. The amount involved is approximately 5×10^{45} ergs.

Since the rotation of the sun is braked through the torque exerted by the magnetic field, it is natural to suggest that most of the energy of rotation passes into magnetic energy by the twisting process that results. We then suppose that this energy is dissipated in flares or electromagnetic solar activity. One outcome of this activity will be the acceleration of particles to high energy. These particles will be mostly protons, which may go up to energies of the order of a billion volts, as in the cosmic rays that come from the present-day sun.

Of course, one wishes to know what fraction of the energy comes out in the form of high speed particles. Some of the larger solar flares have been seen to convert magnetic energy to particle energy with surprising efficiency. Hence it does not seem unreasonable to suggest that somewhere between 1 and 10% of the energy of rotation of the sun may have been converted into energetic solar cosmic rays. The sun may therefore have emitted something in the vicinity of 10^{44} ergs in the form of highly accelerated protons.

Thus we have the following picture. The outflow of gas from the inner regions of the solar system has left behind metric-sized objects. While this has gone on, flares on the sun have emitted high speed protons which will strike these objects. This bombardment can produce interesting nuclear changes in the material composing the bodies. A detailed consideration of the nuclear changes which affect the deuterium, lithium, beryllium, boron, C^{13}, N^{15}, and perhaps I^{129} are considered in the discussion by Fowler in this volume.

There are also some arguments from nuclear physics which affect our estimate of the size of the small objects, quite independent of the argument about the viscous drag of the gas. Although there may be as much as 10^{44} ergs in the form of high speed protons, they cannot be wasted. That is, the changes of a high energy proton striking one of the small objects must not be too small, which would be the case if the objects had condensed into a few large planets. The material must be sufficiently finely divided. It turns out that the radius of the objects should not be greater than about 10 meters.

There is a further consideration that gives a lower limit to the size. Not all the material that formed the meteorites and the terrestrial planets can have been irradiated by the high energy particles, although it appears that there is clear evidence for the irradiation of some of it. If all the material were irradiated, then a few isotopes of some elements would be removed entirely by capture of the neutrons released by the high energy bombardment. For instance, the isotope Gd^{157} has a very large neutron capture cross section and would be entirely lost if every bit of material that went to form the earth were exposed to bombardment.

The natural way of preventing all the material from being exposed to the bombardment is for the objects to be large enough so that the incoming protons will affect only the surface skin. If they are large enough, their interiors will not be significantly irradiated. One can estimate that only about a tenth of the material must be irradiated. The skin depth is fixed by the depth of penetration of a proton with an energy of 1 bev or a little less, which is somewhat less than a meter. Hence for an object to have 90% of its material inside this skin depth, it must have a size of about 10 meters.

It has been pointed out, particularly by Anders and his colleagues, that artificial radioactivity may play a major role in the melting of primitive objects in the early history of the solar system. It is clear that large amounts of radioactivity will be produced by the bombardment processes which have been mentioned. These activities may be responsible not only for the melting that has been associated with the meteorites, but also may play a significant role in further aggregation processes by heating the metric planetesimals and causing them to adhere more readily. The 10^{44} ergs of high energy particles released by the sun and which bombard the metric planetesimals may be compared with the amount of energy required to melt the whole of the material of these terrestrial planets. The latter energy is lower by some 4 or 5 powers of 10. Since it is evident that, cosmogonically speaking, significant amounts of energy may be stored as radioactivities with half-lives up to a few million years, this may play a big role not only in supplying heat but perhaps in other radiation processes as well.

It may take some 10^7 years for the solar nebula to be fully dissipated. One must, therefore, inquire whether any difficulty will arise with the twisting of the magnetic field that links the nebula with the sun. A very large number of twists can be accumulated between the sun and the nebula in 10^7 years. For every turn of the sun within the nebula, there is an additional wrapping of the magnetic field lines that must be accumulated somewhere.

It is not possible simply to store the turns of the magnetic field in the space between the sun and the nebula. This would build up magnetic pressures that could not be stored. Indeed, all the turns of the magnetic field could not be stored within the gaseous disk itself, unless it were an exceptionally massive disk. Then the full number of turns of the magnetic field would build up so high a magnetic pressure that the disk itself would be exploded.

We must therefore consider whether the turns can be stored inside the body of the sun itself. For this purpose it is interesting to calculate the stress at the surface, and the normal pressure exerted by the magnetic field. It turns out that this pressure changes sign when the magnetic lines of force make an angle of more than $45°$ to the normal. That is to say, as soon as the angle exceeds $45°$, the normal pressure changes from outward to inward. Even if one were to start with a more or less radial field, after one or two turns the lines of force would slope at a sufficiently large angle to the normal so that an inward pressure would develop.

This inward pressure would wind the turns in the magnetic field on to the surface of the star just as one might wind a piece of thread on a cylinder. One may expect these turns to be buried inside the star, provided the star is convective. Stars of smaller mass have outer regions that are convective. Such convective motions may bury the lines of force and thus prevent a large magnetic pressure from building up on the surface of the star which would eventually change the direction of the force outward once again.

Another possibility is that the lines might slip over the poles. The magnetic field would then become a very complicated mess with perhaps some knots. There will certainly be a torque. Eventually, even in the knots at the poles, there will be crowded so many lines of force that these will begin to swell. A very complicated situation would clearly arise.

My own speculation is that the lines of force may become stored in the stars of smaller mass. But in the early type stars, of larger mass, there is only a very thin skin available at the surface, and eventually, when that skin is filled up, a high surface magnetic pressure must be built up. This would result in an accumulation of the lines of force between the surface of the star and the gaseous disk so that eventually that disk would break away because of the very large pressure. There seems to be some observational evidence that this type of phenomenon occurs in such stars as those of the Pleiades.

Dissipation of the Solar Nebula

E. OPIK

Department of Physics and Astronomy, University of Maryland, College Park, Maryland

Hoyle's calculations are correct insofar as Spitzer's formula of rate of escape is concerned, but the formula is not applicable in this case if a real solar nebula has formed.

Let us assume a nebula which extends out to the orbit of Uranus, with a density in the central plane somewhere between 10^{10} and 10^{11} molecules/cm^3 and at a temperature high enough to permit the escape of material. In this case the time scale of escape theoretically does not depend on the position of the escape layer but only on the temperature (a velocity factor) over the acceleration due to gravity, and a factor $e^{-E}(1 + E)$. Here E is the ratio of the escape energy to kT, or $mv^2/2kT$.

If this formula is to provide escape in a sufficiently short interval of time, E must be of the order of a few units, say 5. If E is assumed to be 20 the time scale will be too long.

However if we assume E to be equal to 5, we obtain temperatures between 500° and 1000°K which is much higher than radiative equilibrium ($6000°\text{K}/R^{1/2}$, where R is the distance from the sun). These low temperatures give escape in ten million years.

In true escape there must be an exospheric layer in which the process actually takes place. The magic of this formula lies in the fact that the position of the exospheric layer is irrelevant to the calculation of the rate of escape. When the density is large, the exospheric layer extends to a great distance where the gravitational potential is less.

With the densities we have selected (10^{10}–10^{11}) and assuming 2×10^{-15} cm^2 as the cross section for collisions, 5×10^{14} molecules/cm^2 are re-

quired to stop the molecules kinetically. This means that the mean free
path is in the order of 1 km which places the escape layer very far out.

When the escape layer is very far out, those regions below it are gov-
erned by the Boltzmann thermodynamic formula. The density of the gas
somewhere near infinity will be $10^{10} \times e^{-E}$. If E is 5, the factor is 1/100.
This means that at infinity the density of the gas will be 10^8 molecules/cm^3.

In this case we have an infinite body of gas, that is, an imbedded condensation in an infinite nebula, and therefore there is actually no such
escape as depicted by Spitzer's formula.

This does not mean that escape is impossible. When this nebula is placed
in a vacuum and heated sufficiently the density at infinity cannot be
finite. The nebula simply blows off, which is not the evaporation escape
that has been under consideration.

In evaporation escape the picture is different. In a regular nebula E
cannot be 5 or something of that order for the bulk of its mass because if
it were it would extend to infinity. A real nebula of 10^{10} molecules/cm^3
density can be maintained in equilibrium if the temperature is lower, say
20°K or even less. This is made possible by the dust in the nebular plane
which shields the solar radiation. This condition exists, of course, only as
long as the dust exists.

Just as in the terrestrial atmosphere, escape can only take place from
an exospheric layer which is not at infinity. This is no longer Spitzer's
model with an isothermal distribution, but rather a cold gas which has a
hot top.

The escape from this hot top per unit time equals the product

$$U \rho e^{-E}(1 + E),$$

where U is the escape velocity and ρ is the density of this layer. To obtain
the density of this layer we divide the number load of the exosphere, i.e.,
the number of screening molecules, 5×10^{14} molecules/cm^2, by the scale
height. The scale height is not small; it is of the order of the radius of the
nebula, approximately R/E.

If E is taken as equal to 5, the scale height is one-fifth of the radius.
In the hot atmosphere the scale height is of the order of 10^{14} cm, and the
number density can be only 5 molecules/cm^3. If E equals 5, $U e^{-E}(1 + E)$
is 10^3 cm/sec, which is an effective flow velocity and not an escape velocity.
The escape rate becomes 5×10^3 molecules/cm^2/sec, which is an insignificant quantity and cannot have any effect on a cosmic scale.

Thus two models are possible: (i) true escape and (ii) a blowing-off
process.

Escape works only in a cold nebula and does not lead to noticeable effects at all. When the dust clears up and when the nebula becomes hotter, the nebula expands approaching infinity and the second model comes into importance and any amount of gas can blow off the top. This process, however, does not lead to any separation of the gaseous components.

Neither of these models permits the separation of molecules. Neither the "blowing-off" model nor the "escape" model can account for the separation of such quantities of hydrogen and helium from the rest of the elements in the nebula. The separation that we are considering can only be accomplished if part of the hydrogen and helium condense into the solid phase.

Formation of Light Nuclei

WILLIAM A. FOWLER

Kellogg Radiation Laboratory, California Institute of Technology, Pasadena, California

Professor Hoyle has proposed that about 1% of the rotational energy of the early solar system was dissipated in the form of high energy particles, and some of the nuclear effects of these high energy particles substantially support Hoyle's point of view.

The problem of the formation of the light nuclei is well known to most people in the field. In the main sequence stars, where the conversion of hydrogen into helium not only supplies the energy by which these stars shine but, from the point of view of some of us, creates the helium that exists in our system, the equilibrium ratio of deuterium to hydrogen is approximately 10^{-17}, whereas in the oceanic waters of the earth the ratio is 1.5×10^{-4}.

In red giant stars, the Salpeter-Hoyle process, by which helium is converted into carbon–12 through the intermediary of a well-known excited state in carbon-12, solves the problem that has been a specter for some years; the non-existence of mass 5 and mass 8. But it also precludes lithium 6, lithium 7, beryllium 9, boron 10, and boron 11. Yet deuterium and these five other nuclei exist in our system. The question is where did they come from.

Nearly everyone who has thought about the problem agrees that some kind of model is needed in which a high energy source of particles bombards a cool, quiescent medium and produces the light nuclei by spallation processes at such a temperature that the reactions by which these are destroyed in stellar interiors are not operative.

The model that Hoyle has proposed holds at the stage where the sun had left behind the planetary nebula and was coupled to it by a magnetic field about which I concede there is a great deal of argument. The dissipation of the rotational energy in magnetic flares at the surface of the sun expended at least 1% of the energy in high-energy particles. The model makes extremely efficient use of this energy. The high energy particles do not move out isotropically into space, but spiral around the magnetic lines of force of the approximate dipole field, and always pass through the nebular material in the equatorial disk where they produce the light nuclei and the deuterium by spallation and associated processes.

When Hoyle's model came to the attention of Professor Jesse Greenstein and the present author, we looked again to see what could be said from the nuclear standpoint about the production of these nuclei. At first, it would be expected that the abundances of the light nuclei would be proportional to their rate of production in the method of synthesis under discussion. To be specific, the abundances should be proportional to the corresponding spallation production cross-sections in the interaction of protons with an energy spectrum having an effective energy near 500 Mw with such nuclei as oxygen, silicon, and magnesium which constituted the main bulk of the heavy nuclei in the primordial nebular material. The effective energy of 500 Mev was chosen because it is the characteristic energy of high particles ejected from magnetic flares on the surface of the present-day sun.

The "observed" terrestrial and meteoritic abundances are as follows. On the Suess-Urey scale, the abundance of Si^{28} is taken as 10^6, the Li^6 abundance is 7.4, Li^7 is 92.6, Be^9 is 20, B^{10} is 4.5, and B^{11} is 19.5. It will be immediately clear that these abundances are quite remarkable on the basis of proportionality to spallation production cross-sections. I am not prepared to state what the actual spallation production cross sections under these circumstances would be, because there is not sufficient experimental evidence on the subject. My own estimate is that the production cross sections are all approximately equal to 15 millibarns. The important point is that one would not expect them to vary in such a way that Li^7 would be so high in abundance relation to Be^9 and B^{11}, nor that Li^6 and B^{10} would be so low. No doubt there are people who think that the production cross sections might well vary in this capricious way. Hoyle, Greenstein, and I think *not*, and moreover have noted that there are certain other relevant nuclear processes which seem to have just the required cross sections. The cross section of the thermal (n, α) reaction on Li^6 as has been known almost since the beginning of nuclear physics, is approximately 1000 barns. The cross section for $Li^7(n, \alpha)$ is 33, and $Li^7(n, \alpha)$ does not occur for low energy neutrons since it is endonergic. The cross section for $B^{10}(n, \alpha)$ is 4000 barns while the (n, α) cross sections for Be^9 and B^{11} are the order of 10 millibarns and the (n, α) reactions do not occur at low energy for these nuclei.

Furthermore, it is a remarkable fact that when B^{10} is bombarded with neutrons in the laboratory, α particles are released and Li^7 is produced.

If the, at the same time that the spallation process is going on, light nuclear products were being irradiated with neutrons, the (n, α) reactions on Li^6 and on B^{10} would deplete the Li^6, deplete the B^{10}, and enhance Li^7. The observed abundances clearly correspond to these expectations.

The presence of the neutrons is not entirely surprising because at the same time that Li^6, B^{10}, and Li^7 are being produced by spallation processes, neutrons are also being produced, and in copious quantity. These neutrons usually are thermalized at approximately $150°K$. The cross sections just given hold for $300°K$, but they vary roughly as $1/v$, and in fact become even somewhat larger. If the neutrons that are produced simultaneously in the spallation are thermalized, they will do the job of depleting Li^6 and B^{10} and enhancing Li^7.

It does not seem possible for the light nuclei to have been produced with neutrons. Assume Li^6 and Li^7 are produced equally in spallation. If the material was then irradiated with neutrons to such an extent that Li^6 was reduced to 7.4 relative to 92.6 for Li^7, then B^{10} would be completely wiped out. Clearly the process must be simultaneous so that a linear relation between the cross section and the final abundance is obtained rather than an exponential relationship. This is a type of argument that one can now begin to use; namely, that neutron irradiation was simultaneous with production and not a process that happened to terrestrial lithium and boron *after* it had been produced.

The differential equation for the growth of Li^6 can be written as follows:

$$\frac{d(Li^6)}{dn} = \alpha_6 - \frac{\sigma_6(Li^6)}{\Sigma_A N_A \sigma_A} = \alpha_6 - \frac{\sigma_6}{\Sigma}(Li^6) \tag{1}$$

The number of neutrons, n, produced in spallation is used as the running variable. Then for every neutron produced there will be a certain production of Li^6. This will be proportional to what I call α_6, which is nothing more than the yield of Li^6 relative to neutrons averaged over the energy spectrum of the high energy particles—mostly protons—which interact with the target nuclei, oxygen, silicon, and magnesium. These had been produced from hydrogen in nucleosynthesis in the galaxy before the solar system formed.

The ratio α_6 is something like 1/10. In addition, one must take into account the fact that Li^6 is being depleted in proportion to the cross section for the Li^6 (n, α) reaction, times the number of lithium sixes, divided by the sum of all abundances, N_A in the material, times their reaction cross sections, σ_A, with neutrons. The atomic mass A is a convenient reference index. This is merely to say that Li^6 interacts with a fraction of the neutrons, proportional to its cross section and its abundance, relative to all the abundances and cross sections involved. We assume that all of the neutrons interact before decaying.

The light nuclei are very rare. The deuterium relative to hydrogen is rare. It does not require much argument to show that the initial material, which was bombarded, was not changed very much. In other words, $\Sigma_A N_A \sigma_A$ is a constant, during the run of the primary spallation and secondary neutron process, so it can be designated by the symbol, Σ. Then the differential equation is one that even a nuclear physicist can integrate:

$$Li^6 = (\alpha_6 \Sigma / \sigma_6)[1 - \exp(-\sigma_6 n / \Sigma)] \tag{2}$$

Similar equations, differential and integrated, can be written for the other light nuclei. Similar numerical results are obtained so we will work with equation (2).

It develops that the exponent $(\sigma_6 n / \Sigma)$ is approximately equal to 4 so

$$Li \approx \alpha_6 \Sigma / \sigma_6 = \alpha_6 n \Sigma / n \sigma_6 \tag{3}$$

or

$$n / \Sigma \approx (1 / \sigma_6)(Li_S{}^6 / Li^6) \tag{4}$$

In the algebra just accomplished, I have introduced the number of neutrons n, so that it is possible to introduce $Li_S{}^6 = \alpha_6 n$. This is the number of Li^6 produced in the primary spallation process. Then one easily obtains equation (4) for n / Σ, which is the time integrated neutron flux for the over-all irradiation to which terrestrial and meteoritic material was subjected during the formation of the solar system. Assuming that all light nuclei were produced equally in the primary spallation,

$$Li_S{}^6 = (7.4 + 92.6 + 20.0 + 4.5 + 19.5) \div 5 \approx 30.$$

With $Li^6 = 7.4$, less than 30, because of the secondary neutron irradiation, one has $Li_S{}^6 / Li^6 \approx 4$. If we assume σ_6 1000 barns $= 10^{-21}$ cm^2, then equation (4) yields:

$$n / \Sigma = 4 \times 10^{21} \text{ neutrons/cm}^2 \tag{5}$$

Therefore, the approximation $\exp(-\sigma_6 n / \Sigma) \ll 1$ is justified. In our calculations we assumed the time of irradiation to be comparable to the Kelvin-Helmholtz contraction time for the solar system, namely 10^7 years or 3×10^{14} seconds. In round numbers then, the neutron flux must have been:

$$\phi_n \sim 10^7 \text{ neutrons/cm}^2\text{-sec} \tag{6}$$

This flux is more than 10^7 times as great as the present ratio of neutron emission by the sun measured at the earth. However, 10^7 neutrons/cm^2

sec. is not an "impossible" value; in a reactor thermal column it can be as high as 10^{10}.

If all of this is correct, one can immediately determine how much deuterium was produced. The cross section for the $H(n, \alpha)D$ reaction is 0.33 barn, so from this process alone one finds:

$$D/H \sim 0.33 \times 10^{-24} \times 4 \times 10^{21} \qquad (7)$$

$$\sim 1.3 \times 10^{-3}$$

If the primary spallation production to deuterium is included, then this value is increased to:

$$D/H \approx 1.5 \times 10^{-3} \qquad (8)$$

which is just 10 times what is observed in terrestrial oceanic waters.

When our calculations reached this stage we were overjoyed because for years we have been trying to calculate D/H, and we always got numbers like 10^{-17}. It was a very happy circumstance when we got 10 times too much this time.

Then we began to realize that this factor of 10 was quite significant. It is very clear from the nuclear composition of our system that not all of the material was subjected to the amount of neutron flux given by equation (5). For example, the cross section of U^{235}, which has some important applications in our society, is approximately 600 barns. If U^{235} from Galactic nucleosynthesis had been irradiated with 4×10^{21} neutrons/cm^2, it would have been substantially reduced in abundance. Gd^{157} with a cross section of 2.4×10^{5} barns would not have survived at all. Its abundance is certainly "normal" to better than 25%.

The obvious answer is that only 10% of the material was irradiated and then mixed with material that was not irradiated, so that the D/H ratio comes out 1.5×10^{-4} rather than 1.5×10^{-3} and no nucleus could be depleted by more than 10%. Clearly 10% of the material was so situated that it could be reached by the high-energy protons which have a range limited to approximately 80 grams/cm^2 of material because of nuclear interactions. The remaining 90% must be shielded by the irradiated material. As a sample calculation, assume that only 10% of the material was irradiated in the surface layers of a set of planetesimals of standard size. If one sets this surface layer equal to 80 gm/cm^2 or approximately 40 cm at density ~ 2 gm/cm^2 and writes:

$$4/3\pi R^3 = 10 \times 4\pi\lambda R^2 \qquad (9)$$

where $\lambda = 40$ cm is the surface thickness, then one finds that R, the radius of the planetesimals, is 10 meters, which is the same number that Hoyle gave on the basis of quite different considerations. One must realize that

10% of the material could have been in bodies with radii smaller than 40 cm, and the remainder in bodies considerably larger.

However, one does not have complete flexibility in the matter of the size of the planitesimals. If Hoyle's model is followed, then while the gas is being swept out, the planetesimals must not also be swept away. I do not know really how good Professor Hoyle's calculation is, but I suspect it is correct as usual. He insists that planetesimals much less than 1 meter in diameter would be swept along with the gas, so one has a lower limit on the size of the bodies that eventually aggregated in some unknown way to form the earth. This implies some kind of a higher size limit of approximately 100 meters.

The next point is that one can calculate the abundance of hydrogen during spallation and neutron irradiation. One can see in a physical way why this can be done. If there has been too much hydrogen, it would capture all the neutrons and the neutron irradiation would not deplete the Li^6 and B^{10}. If there had been too little, then there exists no proper thermalizing agent. When the calculation is made on this basis, one finds that the hydrogen abundance is 8×10^6, eight times the amount of silicon.

This is a very interesting result, because the hydrogen in the sun on this same scale is 3×10^{10} while the hydrogen on the earth now is 4×10^3. So the irradiation had to happen at an intermediate stage in the hydrogen content of the sun and the hydrogen content on the earth at the present time. There is also the interesting fact that oxygen on the earth now, on this same scale, using the Suess-Urey numbers, is 3.5×10^6. It does not take a chemist to realize that one of the possibilities suggested for the appropriate chemical combination is H_2O. Since the material had to be solid the hydrogen and oxygen were almost certainly retained in the planetesimals as ice.

And so the picture emerges that the planetesimals were largely ice in which grains of magnesium, silicon and iron, were imbedded. They were not cold enough to freeze out ammonia and methane. Hence in terrestrial abundance, $O > \overline{N + C}$. What was the total energy of the primaries? The energy that Hoyle calculated was the original rotational energy of the solar system, 5×10^{45} ergs. If one tries to calculate how much of this energy was dissipated in high-energy particles, then one first notes that about one neutron is produced for every proton, so that integrated proton flux is also 4×10^{21} per cm^2. A half billion or a billion volts are required for each proton or approximately 10^{-3} ergs. The total area irradiated when the planetary material was left behind near the present radius of the orbit of Mercury must have been $\sim 10^{25}$ cm^2. Thus the energy required was $4 \times 10^{21} \times 10^{25} \times 10^{-3}$ ergs $= 4 \times 10^{43}$ ergs or just 1% of the total available energy.

A more detailed calculation shows that there was sufficient energy at 1% efficiency to produce the light nuclei in the earth, and Venus, Mercury, and Mars, but not in Jupiter, Saturn, Uranus, and Neptune, because there is then a factor of 1000 alone in the amount of material irradiated. If the spacemen find deuterium in Jupiter and Saturn, and lithium, beryllium, and boron, then someone will have to suggest another source of energy.

So we predict that one would not find the D/H ratio in Jupiter, for example, to be as high as 1.5×10^4. Furthermore, we would say that D/H is not this high in the interstellar medium, nor will lithium, beryllium, and boron be as abundant as $\sim 10^{-4} Si^6$.

The point that George Herbig raised in connection with his work on the T-Tauri stars led us to inquire whether the lithium, beryllium, and boron in the sun could have been made by spallation, since at the same time that the sun was bombarding the planetary material, it also was bombarding its own surface material. It develops that the spallation probably contaminated a convective layer in the surface of the sun equal to about 10% of the total mass of the sun.

Clearly, one must say that as the sun came on to the main sequence, it did not develop excessive luminosity for a period of time. The planetary material must be in the solid state to thermalize the neutrons and also to shield the internal material from the high energy particles. The sun could have grown hotter *after* the period in which it was most active magnetically.

It is well known that the ratio of lithium to beryllium in the sun is only approximately 1% of the terrestrial and meteoritic value. The only lithium that survives in the sun is that which is produced in the last convective cycle, because if Li^6 and Li^7 are convected deep enough in the stellar interior, they are destroyed by (p, α) reactions. Thus we would say that the lithium which Greenstein and Bonsack find in the T-Tauri stars has not yet been destroyed, i.e., the T-Tauri stars have not yet gone through a surface convective stage where their lithium was reduced. Again a very essential point is noted in the case of the sun: that production and depletion must have been simultaneous. Otherwise the 1% is just an accident. If the lithium was already in the material that formed the sun, and it was depleted by mixing down to a region with a temperature near 3×10^6 degrees, it would be very difficult to understand why the exponential depletion stopped at 1%. On the other hand, if depletion and production are simultaneous, it is very easy to obtain this value.

One of the dividends from these considerations is the very beautiful results that have been obtained by Reynolds, Murthy, and Anders, and other people in geochemistry and geophysics, who have studied the relationship between the isotopic anomalies in certain meteorites and those in the earth.

Reynolds has found the abundance of Xe^{129} relative to the total Xe to be greater than that in atmospheric Xe. Xe^{129} is the decay product of I^{129} which has a mean life time of 2.5×10^7 years. Reynolds suggests that a small amount of I^{129} was retained in the meteoritic material and subsequently decayed to produce the Xe^{129} anomaly. It will be clear that the interval between production of the I^{129} and its retention in meteoritic material cannot exceed several mean life times if a reasonable fraction of the original I^{129} is to be retained. Similarly, Murthy finds an anomaly in meteoritic Ag^{107} which he attributed to the decay of Pd^{107} with a mean life time of 10^7 years. Anders and his colleagues suggest radioactive Al^{26}, with a mean life time of only 10^6 years, was the source of heat which partially melted and fractionated the parent bodies of the meteorites. Thus various significant events occurred in the solar system within several times 10^6 to 10^8 years after the final nucleosynthesis of Al^{26}, Pd^{107}, and I^{129}. From the conventional point of view that these nuclei were formed in the evolving stars of the Galaxy prior to the formation of the solar system, these time intervals seem very short indeed. Mixing of synthesized material throughout a reasonable portion of the galaxy alone requires more than 10^8 years. On the other hand, the time scale of the formation of the solar system, 10^7 years, is a quite acceptable interval and detailed calculations with observed or reasonable estimated cross sections indicate that quite sufficient quantities of Al^{26}, Pd^{107}, and I^{129} were produced by the spallation and/or neutron irradiation which has been under discussion.

In conclusion it must be emphasized that any model proposed must be consistent with the nuclear ground rules. Hoyle's model seems to survive the tests required by what nuclear clues we have to the events which transpired.

GENERAL REFERENCES

1. Fowler, W. A., Greenstein, J. L., and Hoyle, F., *Geophys. J.* **6**, 148 (1962); *Am. J. Phys.* **29**, 393 (1961).
2. Fowler, W. A., *Science* **135**, 1037 (1962).

The Formation of the Solar Nebula

A. G. W. CAMERON

Institute for Space Studies, Goddard Space Flight Center, National Aeronautics and Space Administration, New York

I should like to start by discussing some of the difficulties that exist in the picture that has been presented by Fowler and by Hoyle. Let us see what seem to be the fundamental points of their analysis. Hoyle takes the minimum amount of mass in the solar nebula required to give the present amount of angular momentum to the planets. His whole cosmogony develops from this concept. It turns out, according to Fowler, that this is also an absolute upper limit on the mass that can be present and allow his nuclear transformations to take place. Fowler's nuclear arguments are based on the observation that there is a tremendous amount of deuterium in the earth and in the meteorites and that there are surprisingly small amounts of the isotopes Li^6 and B^{10}, which have the high neutron capture cross-sections, relative to the other lithium, beryllium, and boron isotopes. These statements seem to be the essence of the Fowler-Greenstein-Hoyle cosmogony.

Let us first consider some of the nuclear aspects of the situation. Primordial helium has now been extracted from quite a number of different chondritic meteorites, and in this the ratio of He^3 to He^4 has been found to lie in the range 3 to 4×10^{-4}, with no evidence that there is any real variation in this ratio at all. If one adopts typical stellar ratios of hydrogen to helium, and the terrestrial ratio of deuterium to hydrogen, and assume that this deuterium-to-hydrogen ratio is also characteristic of the primitive solar nebula, then it follows that the amount of He^3 in the primitive solar nebula should have been less than the amount of deuterium by only a factor of about 3. This means there was a tremendous amount of primordial He³, since even on the Fowler-Greenstein-Hoyle model there is no way of producing the constant ratio of He³ to He⁴ by spallation reactions within their small planetesimal bodies. The amount of primordial He⁴ gas trapped in different meteorites varies enormously, and there should be no relation between this and the radiation exposure of the meteorites. Furthermore, Fowler's thermal neutrons should be very effective in destroying He³ produced by spallation, and indeed the presence of such He³ would destroy his calculations on the neutron budget.

Furthermore, it should be pointed out that the abundances of lithium, beryllium, and boron in the Suess-Urey table, upon which Fowler's calculations are based, are extremely uncertain. This was emphasized by Suess and Urey in their basic paper on abundances. We are now starting to get some better analytical values for the abundances of these light elements in chondritic meteorites. Fireman has found that the abundance of lithium is only one-third of the amount given by Suess and Urey. Even more spectacular is the recent work of C. W. Sill, who has found the average abundance of beryllium in many chondrites to be less than in the table of Suess and Urey by a factor of 30! On the Suess–Urey scale, the abundance of beryllium should not be 20, but 0.6. The significance of this measurement is that despite the fact that beryllium has an extremely small neutron capture cross-section, its actual abundance is much less than those of the isotopes Li⁶ and B¹⁰. This destroys the entire basis for Fowler's neutron capture analysis.

One must delve deeper and ask whether spallation reactions in the primitive solar nebula are the only ways of making the necessary amounts of deuterium, He³, lithium, beryllium, and boron. Many other possible mechanisms exist; the question as to whether any of them can be quantitatively sufficient to account for the lithium, beryllium, and boron in the earth and meteorites has not yet been investigated fully. I am an advocate of the view that the terrestrial deuterium-to-hydrogen ratio is approximately the ratio between these two isotopes that one should expect to find in the interstellar medium, although quite probably one should reduce the amount of deuterium by a factor of 3 or so, to account for galactic evolution effects since the time of formation of the solar system. In my view, the manufacture of deuterium should inevitably accompany the explosion of Type II supernovae.

Most theories of such a supernova event start with the implosion of the core of a massive star in an advanced stage of evolution, in which nuclear reactions have converted the central material into iron and its neighboring elements. In my own analysis of this situation, the implosion should continue until the material at the center has reached nuclear densities, and under such circumstances the iron should be converted first to helium, then to neutrons and protons, and then to mostly neutrons with some admixture of hyperons. The shock wave which rebounds from this implosion should cause the ejection of some of the neutron material.

When a neutron gas expands rapidly into space, some of the neutrons undergo β decay to form protons, after the expansion has gone on long enough for the gas to have become rather cold, and these protons then capture further neutrons to form deuterium and possibly tritium. In the early stages of the expansion, the density should be sufficiently high for the capture chain to produce tritium. However, in the later stages of the expansion, the neutron capture does not go further than the formation of deuterium, owing to the fact that the neutron capture cross-section of hydrogen is much greater than that of deuterium. With a gas expansion velocity typical of that observed in Type II supernovae, one can expect a typical deuterium-to-tritium ratio of about 3. This is quite consistent with the deuterium-to-tritium ratio inferred from the meteorite data, and also with a large abundance of these two isotopes in the interstellar medium.

The same kind of supernova ejection process may possibly also be responsible for the formation of at least some of the isotopes of lithium, beryllium, and boron. This may occur in the boundary layer region of the imploded gas in which the composition has changed to a mixture of He^4 and neutrons. Under conditions of nuclear statistical equilibrium, there would also be small amounts of the lithium, beryllium, and boron isotopes, and some of these abundances may be frozen in the expanding gas. These questions have been very inadequately examined. In addition, further amounts of Li^7 may be formed and small steady-state amounts preserved in stars in which deep outer convection zones go down deep enough for hydrogen burning by the proton-proton chain to take place. Further amounts of this isotope may be formed when a supernova shock wave goes through a region of the stellar envelope that contains some He^3 and He^4. Clearly we have not reached the stage where we must conclude, as an act of desperation, that the only possible way of forming the lithium, beryllium, and boron is by some sort of spallation mechanism in the solar nebula.

A further consequence of the Fowler–Greenstein–Hoyle picture is the prediction that some 10% of nonvolatile material has been subjected to an intense neutron flux, which should have destroyed the heavy isotopes that have large neutron capture cross-sections. Fowler, Greenstein, and Hoyle argue that the material that has gone into the formation of the earth has been thoroughly mixed, and the complete depletion of certain isotopes in 10% of the material becomes insignificant when all the material is mixted together; the 10% depletion in the abundances of certain isotopes is an effect that goes far beyond the ability of theories of nucleogenesis to predict actual abundances of isotopes. Possibly this would be so for the earth, but it is highly questionable whether the meteorites can be considered to be similarly well-mixed bodies. Indeed, both Suess and Wood believe that the condrules in the chondritic meteorites represent direct condensations from the primordial gas of the solar nebula. Hence, in the meteorites one should expect significant variations in the abundances within their elements of heavy isotopes having large neutron capture cross-sections. Rama Murthy has looked very hard for such variations, and he has not found any. This is certainly an embarrassment for the Fowler–Greenstein–Hoyle picture.

For these reasons, I believe that Fowler's nuclear arguments certainly do not compel us to believe in the necessity for a solar nebula of very small mass. Thus, if a theory of the formation of the solar nebula gives us a very large amount of gas in the nebula, then one should not say that it is a strong argument against such a nebula that Fowler's nuclear reactions cannot take place in it.

Let us turn to the question of the formation of the solar nebula itself. Let me start with some comments on the picture that was outlined by Lyman Spitzer. He discussed the conditions required for an average interstellar cloud to become gravitationally unstable, and he went on to discuss the processes that come into operation during the collapse of such a cloud. He found that the magnetic energy density in such a cloud was too high to allow the fragmentation of it to carry on very far and for the fragments to approach stellar masses. Hence, in his view it is necessary that such a collapsing cloud hang up before it gets to the final stage of stellar fragmentation, and this period of suspended animation is supposed to continue long enough for most of the magnetic field to escape from the gas. Clearly this is one of the most interesting and also uncertain stages in Spitzer's discussion.

It has seemed to me somewhat unlikely that star formation should start from an average interstellar cloud such as is assumed by Spitzer. From the virial theorem we can see that it is much easier for a dense interstellar cloud to become gravitationally unstable than for an average one to do so. Much smaller total masses are required for gravitational instability in such a cloud. Hence I believe that we should more profitably discuss how star formation might start from an interstellar cloud possessing the highest observed density of material in space. There is observational evidence for gas densities as high as 1000 hydrogen atoms per cubic centimeter or more in some clouds.

There is no reason to believe that the magnetic field energy in such a dense cloud should be any higher than that generally existing in the interstellar medium surrounding it. Presumably, dense clouds have to be formed by the compression of the gas along the magnetic lines of force. Indeed, from the point of view of pressure equilibrium, the magnetic field density inside a dense cloud may be somewhat less than that in the surroundings. If there is a significantly large magnetic field in the interstellar medium, of the order of 10^{-5} gauss, then magnetic pressure will dominate most of the interstellar medium. However, the gas pressure in a very dense cloud would tend to exceed that of the magnetic pressure, and hence such a cloud would tend to expand until it was contained roughly by the excess magnetic pressure on its boundary. If one considers star formation starting with the collapse of a cloud of this sort, then many of the difficulties mentioned by Spitzer do not arise.

In the first place, the ratio of magnetic energy to gravitational potential energy in such a dense cloud is very much smaller than in the case of Spitzer's average cloud. It turns out that the magnetic energy density does not limit the fragmentation process until the mass of the fragments has become of the order of one solar mass or somewhat less. Hence there is no need for the collapse of the cloud to be halted for a period during which the magnetic field can escape from the gas.

Furthermore, when one starts with a very dense cloud, its rotational energy is very small, if one assumes that the period of the rotation of the cloud is the same as that of its revolution around the center of the galaxy. During the contraction of such a cloud to the point where opacity halts fragmentation, the amount of angular momentum transmitted to the external medium owing to the rotation of the cloud as a whole is very small, since the cloud only twists about a quarter of a revolution. Hence, in this stage of the contraction, the transmission of angular momentum to the external medium cannot be very important.

For these reasons, it seems to me to be reasonable to expect that a dense interstellar cloud may collapse to form stellar fragments of the order of a solar mass or less, without having been checked short of the final stage of collapse. There is no reason to believe that any appreciable quantity of the angular momentum possessed by the original cloud has been transmitted to the surrounding medium. Most of the angular momentum has gone into the orbital motion of the stellar fragments about their center of mass, and we can expect that the rotation of the fragments can be calculated by assuming that there is local conservation of angular momentum in that portion of the cloud which goes to form the individual fragments.

Following the formation of such fragments, there is a short period of Kelvin–Helmholtz contraction, following which a further period of collapse is reached when the central temperature of the fragments becomes large enough to initiate the dissociation of hydrogen molecules. I do not know how much angular momentum the fragments may lose during this short Kelvin–Helmholtz contraction stage. If the fragments are still connected to the external medium by magnetic lines of force, then some angular momentum may be transmitted to the external medium before turbulence or other mechanisms lead to a severing and reconnection of these lines of force, and the fragments become magnetically isolated from their surroundings. Thus, it seems useful to discuss the situation which one may obtain if either no angular momentum is lost during this stage or much angular momentum is lost during this stage.

Let us first consider the condition in which much angular momentum is lost, and we may neglect any rotational effects in the contracting protostar.

Let us briefly consider what happens to the protostar during the collapse phase. When the central temperature rises to about 1800°K, about half the hydrogen molecules will have become dissociated. Under these conditions, the ratio of specific heats of the gas, γ, decreases. When γ, or a suitably weighted average of γ throughout the star, becomes less than 4/3, the protostar becomes gravitationally unstable, and hence dynamical collapse occurs.

One can make a crude study of what happens by assuming that the protostar can be represented by a polytropic model. I have carried through such a study for two assumptions about the polytrope: (1) that it is a polytrope of index 1.5 representing complete convection; and (2) a polytrope of index 3, roughly representing a body in radiative equilibrium. There is not a great deal of difference between the behavior of these polytropes, and we may simply describe a sort of average behavior of them.

A protostar of one solar mass reaches this critical central temperature when its radius decreases to about 100 a.u. Then the collapse sets in.

During the normal contraction of a star in the Kelvin-Helmholtz stage, and with γ equal to 5/3, half of the released gravitational potential energy is radiated from the surface and half is stored as internal heat. During the collapse stage the excess half of the gravitational potential energy is not radiated from the surface, but instead goes into dissociating hydrogen molecules and ionizing the hydrogen and helium atoms. First, let us consider only the dissociation of the hydrogen molecules. We can get some idea of how far the collapse will go by assuming that the excess half of the gravitational potential energy that would ordinarily be radiated away goes instead into dissociating the hydrogen molecules throughout the protostar. The collapsed model of the protostar would thus have a gravitational potential energy with an absolute value of approximately twice the binding energy of the hydrogen molecules originally within it.

When one makes this assumption, one finds that the collapse associated with the dissociation of the hydrogen molecules will lead to a central temperature of about 30,000°K. However, at this temperature, hydrogen in the central regions of the star is already nearly completely ionized. Hence we cannot expect the collapse to stop with just the dissociation of hydrogen molecules, but it must continue while the ionization of hydrogen takes place.

The collapse goes beyond the stage of hydrogen ionization. One makes this calculation all over again and finds that a configuration with ionized hydrogen has a central temperature more than sufficient to singly ionize helium. Furthermore, when helium is singly ionized throughout most of the star, it is doubly ionized at the center. Hence, one has to find the final configuration by equating the absolute value of half the gravitational potential energy to the sum of the dissociation energy of hydrogen molecules, the ionization energy of hydrogen, and the single and double ionization energies of helium. Such a configuration has a radius of about a third of an astronomical unit. It would collapse to this radius in about a free fall lifetime, or just a few hundred years.

According to Hoyle's point of view, this is where the protostar should start shedding its nebula. The radius of the protosun is about equal to that of the orbit of Mercury, and in Hoyle's view this is where it becomes rotationally unstable at the equator.

Now let us consider what happens on the point of view that the protosun retains the angular momentum it had as part of the original interstellar cloud. It turns out in this case that the protosun becomes rotationally unstable at the equator while it is still in the original Kelvin-Helmholtz contraction stage, before its radius gets down to about 100 a.u. Further contraction must be accompanied by the loss of mass at the equator, which thus allows one to conserve the angular momentum of the system as a whole. One can expect a fairly strong internal magnetic energy in such a protosun and it is probable that this will cause the protosun to rotate rigidly until the dynamical collapse sets in, since any energy that might go into differential rotation in the model would simply strengthen the magnetic field, thus dissipating any differential rotation.

I have carried out some numerical calculations concerning such a collapse starting with rotational instability at the equator. These calculations were done by finding the mass distribution in the polytropic models along cylinders taken about the axis of rotation of the protosun, since the mass on the surfaces of such cylinders should share the same angular velocity. As the collapse progresses, there will be local conservation of angular momentum, and the mass on the surfaces of these cylinders will be shed when its rotational velocity becomes equal to the Kepler rotational velocity owing to the gravitational field of the interior mass. We may expect the local conservation of angular momentum owing to the fact that the collapse is a dynamically violent event. I assumed that the Kepler velocity of each cylindrical mass element could be calculated by assuming that all interior mass is concentrated at the center of the system. This is a very crude assumption, but it is probably sufficient for the purposes of a preliminary investigation.

This leads to one important question: how much of the mass that starts collapsing is not shed but remains to form a central body in hydrostatic equilibrium with most of the hydrogen and helium ionized? It turns out that, for both polytropes, no central body is formed. Only a pure nebula is formed. Hence the gravitational potential energy of the system that has been released has been partly stored as heat and partly as rotational energy throughout the nebula.

I have carried out the numerical calculations for both polytropes with assumed initial masses of 2 and 4 solar masses. These were taken somewhat larger than a solar mass in order to allow for the possibilities of mass ejection that seems to occur in the T Tauri stages of stellar evolution, and also to allow for possible mass ejection by hydrodynamic flows from the resulting solar nebulae.

The mass distributions that one gets in these nebulae are of interest. They are shown in Fig. 1.

Since no central body in hydrostatic equilibrium is formed directly during the collapse, one must presumably form it by magnetic friction within such a nebula. The magnetic field tends to be wound into a tighter

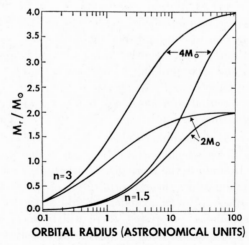

FIG. 1. The nebular mass within various orbital radii.

spiral, and hence the nebula would have to break itself up in order to conserve its own angular momentum, since the differential energy of rotation is dissipated by conversion into magnetic energy. During this process most of the mass would flow inward and a little of the mass would flow outward, carrying with it most of the angular momentum.

One can see from Fig. 1 that one would have to collect a solar mass for the $n = 1.5$ case out to a radius of the order of the orbit of Saturn. In the $n = 3$ case one would have to collect all the mass out to a radius of the order of the orbit of Venus or of the earth. These would be minimal amounts.

Figure 2 shows the surface density of the resulting nebula, namely, the amount of mass that lies above every square centimeter on the surface of the nebular plane. It may be seen that the results are rather insensitive to the total mass that is involved if we have a polytrope of 1.5, but they are somewhat more sensitive to the total mass if the polytrope has an index of 3. Nevertheless, the total amount of the mass involved in this nebula is probably a record for proposals of this kind, namely, one solar mass or more.

This nebula will be formed at high temperatures. The height of the nebula above the central plane will, of course, be a function of this temperature. The pressure in the center will remain roughly the same. Essentially, as the nebula cools, the central portion will cool from high temperatures to low ones at roughly constant pressure. This pressure is thus something that is characteristic of the nebula and hence is a quantity of interest. The pressures calculated for the various cases are shown in Figure 3.

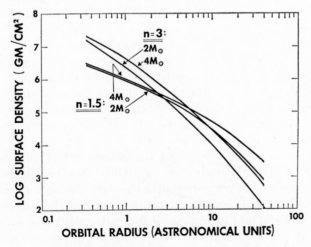

FIG. 2. Surface density in the nebular disk.

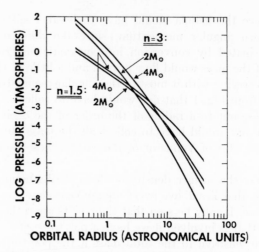

FIG. 3. Pressure at the center of the nebula disk.

These pressures are of interest in some of the calculations that are being carried out by John Wood on the formation of chondrules by direct condensation of the solar nebula. He finds that the liquid field of silicates and iron seems to require a pressure of at least 10^{-2} atm, or possibly a little lower. The interesting thing about the pressures in Fig. 3 is that pressures of this order of magnitude should be available in the nebula out to roughly the vicinity of the asteroidal belt.

Once we have formed a nebular disk of this sort, how long will it take to dissipate? This will depend very much on the strength and character of the magnetic field contained within it, about which we know nothing. However, dissipation may not be terribly long as compared to, say, a time scale of the order of a million years.

The dissipating motions of such a large amount of mass will tend to carry along very small bodies. Actually, the present planets represent only about a 1% efficiency for condensation of the nonvolatile constituents of the nebula. We must accumulate bodies of fairly substantial size, at least of asteroidal size, in order for them to withstand the dissipation of the nebula inwards to form the central sun. Furthermore, such an accumulation would have to take place rather quickly.

This is not the place to consider the details of such processes of accumulation. However, it opens the possibility that the processes of accumulation need not be very efficient, in the sense that only a small amount of the nonvolatile mass is accumulated, and this may help to explain how accumulation could take place possibly in a rather short time scale. Further details of this discussion may be found in the writer's paper on the formation of the sun and planets (A. G. W. Cameron, *Icarus* **1,** 13, 1962).

Meteorites and the Early History of the Solar System[*]

EDWARD ANDERS

Enrico Fermi Institute for Nuclear Studies, and Departments of Chemistry and Geophysical Sciences, University of Chicago, Chicago, Illinois

I. Introduction

Meteorites can contribute in two ways toward a better understanding of the early history of the solar system. First, they seem to provide a more representative sample of average planetary matter than the highly-differentiated crust of the earth. Second, the meteorite parent bodies ceased to be geochemically active very shortly after their formation, some 4.5×10^9 years ago, and the meteorites thus provide a much better preserved record of the earliest events in the formation of the planetary system than does the earth.

Unfortunately, there is no consensus on the nature of the meteorite parent bodies, not even on such basic properties as size, location, and multiplicity (Table I). It is not too surprising that such disagreement exists: the meteorite samples commonly available for study represent only about 10^{-23} to 10^{-26} of the parent body, and some degree of personal bias is inevitable in such a long extrapolation. Given this difference in models, even a simple observation, such as the fact that the iron meteorites were once molten, may occasionally lead to radically different interpretations. Ringwood (1959), Lovering (1957), and Wood (1958) assumed that the melting was caused by long-lived radioactivities (K^{40}, Th^{232}, U^{235}, and U^{238}); Urey attributed it to chemical reactions among thermodynamically

---

[*] The material in this chapter is drawn in part from two papers by the author (Anders, 1962, 1963).

TABLE I

PROPERTIES OF METEORITE PARENT BODIES

	Lovering (1957)	Ringwood (1961)	Urey (1959)	Fish et al. (1960); Wood (1958, 1962a)
Size	Planetary	Lunar	Lunar	Asteroidal
Location	2–5 a.u.	2–5 a.u.	1 a.u.	2–5 a.u.
Number	One	Several	One	Several

unstable compounds (Urey and Donn, 1956) or adiabatic compression of gases (Urey, 1962a); and Fish et al. (1960), following an earlier suggestion by Urey (1955), proposed that extinct radioactivities, specifically 740,000-year Al^{26}, were responsible for the melting. Not many properties of meteorites, however well established, permit only a single, unambiguous interpretation. Hence, the most one can demand of any theory of the origin of the solar system is that it be compatible with the primary properties of the meteorites, and with those secondary deductions on which a consensus exists.

It is not always possible to decide whether a given property reflects a process in the meteorite parent body or in the solar nebula. Even in those cases where the property clearly dates back to the nebular stage, the original record has often been altered by later events in the meteorite parent body, or elsewhere. These limitations of meteoritic evidence must be borne in mind at all times.

A very comprehensive review of the subject was given by Urey (1957a) in Vol. 2 of *Progress in Physics and Chemistry of the Earth*. This paper is still of fundamental importance, although certain ideas contained therein have been modified by Urey in later papers (Urey, 1956, 1957b, 1958, 1959, 1962a). The present chapter is of narrower scope, and deals mainly with evidence obtained since 1957. In some cases, the conclusions reached differ from those of Urey, partly because of the introduction of new evidence, and partly because of differences in point of view.

II. Early Thermal History of Meteoritic Matter

Some important clues can be obtained from the carbonaceous chondrites. They are quite similar to "ordinary" chondrites in bulk composition (Wiik, 1956), except for their higher content of water (10–20% versus

<0.5%) and carbon (1–5% versus <0.1%). Part of the carbon occurs in the form of organic compounds; a fact that has lately enhanced the popular appeal of these meteorites.

A. Mineralogy

The mineralogy of the carbonaceous chondrites is particularly revealing (Table II). The minerals found can be divided into three classes: conventional, "high-temperature" minerals; "characteristic" minerals, peculiar to this class of meteorites; and trace minerals. Estimated relative abundances are given as negative logarithms to the base 2.

One can prove rather convincingly that at least some of the characteristic minerals are alteration products of the high-temperature minerals, rather than vice versa. X-ray diffraction and optical studies of composite grains of olivine $[(Mg, Fe)_2SiO_4]$ and Murray F mineral (a hydrated silicate of Mg and Fe), show that the olivine sometimes occurs in thin parallel plates of the same crystallographic orientation, though the individual plates are separated by a thin layer of exceedingly fine-grained, randomly oriented Murray F mineral. The common orientation of the olivine plates can be understood only if single-crystal olivine served as the starting material for at least that part of the Murray F mineral which is more intimately associated with it (DuFresne and Anders, 1962a).

Many of the other characteristic minerals, too, appear to be hydrated silicates. This fact, and particularly the occurrence of hydrated $MgSO_4$ in distinct veins, suggests that liquid water must once have acted on these meteorites, converting high-temperature minerals to the characteristic minerals. A detailed analysis shows that the observed mineral assemblage is very nearly in a state of chemical equilibrium, corresponding to a pH of 8–10, a reduction potential of ≤ -0.2 volts, and a temperature not far from $300°K$ (DuFresne and Anders, 1962a; Nagy et al., 1962). We shall first attempt to establish the origin of the high-temperature minerals that served as the starting material for the carbonaceous chondrites, and then discuss possible settings for this aqueous stage.

B. Ancestral Material of Carbonaceous Chondrites

Several alternative origins have been proposed for the high-temperature minerals. Edwards and Urey (1955) and Urey (1961) have pointed out that the carbonaceous chondrites have a variable, and frequently lower, content of Na and K than the ordinary chondrites. In the most extreme case, Nogoya, this depletion amounts to a factory of ~4, relative to the

TABLE II

MINERALOGY OF CARBONACEOUS CHONDRITES[a]

(From DuFresne and Anders, 1962)

	Orgueil	Ivuna	Haripura	Cold Bok	Mighei	Murray	Ornans	Lancé	Mokoia
Wiik's Class	I	I	II	II	II	II	III	III	III
Subclass	A	A	B	C	C	C	D	D	E
High-temperature minerals									
Clinopyroxene						3			
Olivine		?	3	3	1	1	0–1	0–1	1
Alpha Iron			9		10	10	7	5	
Gamma Iron								10	
Magnetic Troilite	5	5					5	5	
"Characteristic" minerals									
Orgueil LM	1	1							
Magnetite	1	1	3	3	11[b]	1	?	?	2
Murray F				1	1	1			
Haripura M									
Mokoia HT and SW									5
Epsomite	3	3	6	6	6	6	*>16*	*10*	6
Sulfur	6	6	6	9	9	9	*>20*	*13*	6
Trace minerals									
Dolomite	9	8							
Breunnerite	10								
Pentlandite					11				

[a] Estimated abundances are given as negative logarithms of 2. Thus Mighei is about half olivine and half "Murray F" mineral, with mere traces of iron, pentlandite, magnetite, epsomite, and sulfur. Italicized values are of lower accuracy.

[b] Trace associated with metallic iron.

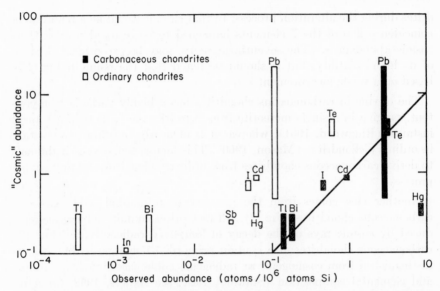

Fig. 1. Trace element abundances in carbonaceous chondrites and ordinary chondrites. [Reproduced from Anders (1963) with permission of the publisher.] Although the ordinary chondrites are strongly depleted in these trace elements, they occur in carbonaceous chondrites in nearly their "cosmic" abundances. This suggests that carbonaceous chondrites are more closely related to primordial matter than the ordinary chondrites. [Data were taken from the following sources: Bi, Hg, Pb, and Tl (Reed *et al.*, 1960; Ehmann and Huizenga, 1959); Cd (Schmitt, 1962); I and Te (Goles and Anders, 1962); In (Schindewolf and Wahlgren, 1960); Sb (Anders, 1960)].

ordinary chondrites. Urey therefore suggested that the carbonaceous chondrites were derived from the ordinary chondrites [specifically, the high-iron group, Fe/Si ≈ 0.85 (Urey and Craig, 1953)], by an alteration process that depleted the alkalis while introducing S, C, and a few other elements in free or combined form.

This picture has become less satisfactory now that the abundances of various trace elements in meteorites have been determined. Most elements occur in meteorites in approximately their "cosmic" abundances, as given by the semi-empirical abundance curves of Suess and Urey (1956) and Cameron (1959a). Other trace elements, including most chalcophile ones, do not conform to this pattern. As discussed more fully in Section IV,B, they occur in approximately their predicted abundances in carbonaceous chondrites, but are depleted by factors of up to 1000 in ordinary chondrites (Fig. 1). If the carbonaceous chondrites were derived from ordinary chondrites, as suggested by Urey, one would have to assume that the depleted elements were somehow added to the carbonaceous chondrites during the alteration process. In that case, it would be a remarkable coincidence if 6 of the 7 elements happened to be restored to just their cosmic abundances. (The seventh, mercury, may be exceptional because of its high volatility, but it should be noted that the point in Fig. 1 is based on a single measurement.)

The olivine in carbonaceous chondrites has a highly variable iron content, ranging in a single meteorite from 3 to 54 mole % FeO in a typical instance (Ringwood, 1961), whereas it is of nearly constant composition in ordinary chondrites (Mason, 1960). This factor, too, makes it difficult to derive carbonaceous chondrites from ordinary chondrites by any simple process.

Another clue comes from the presence of primordial noble gases in carbonaceous chondrites (Fig. 2). All meteorites contain noble gases produced by cosmic rays or the decay of long-lived radioactivities, but the carbonaceous chondrites also contain primordial noble gases that can be distinguished from cosmogenic or radiogenic noble gases by their isotopic and elemental composition (Stauffer, 1961; see Anders, 1962, for a review). With the exception of He^4 and Ar^{40}, most of which is radiogenic, the noble gases in an ordinary chondrite are produced chiefly by the action of cosmic rays on iron, silicon, and other stable elements in the meteorite. For example, the three neon isotopes are made in nearly equal amounts in this process (Eberhardt and Eberhardt, 1961), whereas in primordial neon (represented by neon in the earth's atmosphere) the ratio $Ne^{20}/Ne^{21}/Ne^{22}$ is 90.8/0.26/8.9. The elemental ratios differ too, as can be seen in Fig. 2. The bulk of the primordial noble gases once associated with the matter of the terrestrial planets and the asteroids seems to have been lost at a very early stage in the history of the solar system (Russell and Menzel, 1933; Brown, 1949a; Suess, 1949), and it is surprising that appreciable amounts are still present in some meteorites.

The presence of these gases in a meteorite is not necessarily an assurance of its primitive character; in a few instances substantial amounts have been found in ordinary chondrites and even in such highly differentiated meteorites as achondrites and irons. In some cases at least the trapping of these gases must have occurred in the meteorite parent body, perhaps by shock (Fredriksson, 1962) or by some other mechanism involving an "internal atmosphere" (DuFresne and Anders, 1962b). But the very low abundance of these gases in most ordinary chondrites makes it difficult to derive the carbonaceous from the ordinary chondrites without some *ad hoc* mechanism for the reintroduction of the noble gases.

The trace element abundances, the variations in the olivine composition, and the primordial gas content are most easily explained by assum-

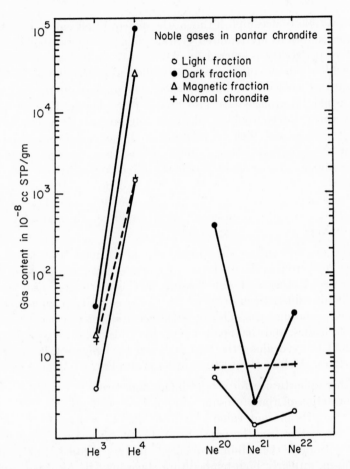

Fig. 2. Noble gases in an ordinary and a carbonaceous chondrite. [Reproduced from Anders (1963) with permission of the publisher.] In Holbrook, these gases (except for radiogenic He⁴) are produced by cosmic-ray induced spallation reactions on iron and other stable nuclides. The three neon isotopes occur in nearly equal abundance. In Murray, the isotopic abundances of Ne and Ar resemble those in the Earth's atmosphere, suggesting that these gases, too, are of primordial origin. A small amount of cosmogenic gas is present in Murray, as indicated by the increased abundances of He³ and Ne²¹ relative to their atmospheric abundances.

ing that both the carbonaceous chondrites and the ordinary chondrites were derived from still more primitive ancestral matter. Perhaps the most difficult fact to explain concerning this material is that some of it at least must have passed through an earlier, high-temperature stage without losing its primordial gases completely.

It is possible to accomplish this in the meteorite parent body, but some special assumptions are required (DuFresne and Anders, 1962b). A more attractive possibility is offered by Wood's (1958, 1962a) hypothesis, according to which planetary matter, expelled from the sun at high initial temperatures, cooled by adiabatic expansion so that progressive condensation could take place (see also Suess, 1948; Levin, 1958). The least volatile constituents would condense to high-temperature minerals (olivine, pyroxene, and nickel-iron). Material passing through the liquid zone of the phase diagram might condense to droplets (chondrules), whereas the remainder would condense directly from gas to solid. The particle size and mineralogical purity would depend on the relative rates of nucleation and growth, as well as on the cooling rate. Other substances, e.g., H_2O, NH_3, and carbon compounds, would condense on further temperature drop.

In the presence of cosmic proportions of H_2 and H_2O, any exposed metallic iron would be converted to magnetite below 600°K (Latimer, 1950; Urey, 1952a) and some hydrated silicates might form from the finely divided dust. Each of these substances could trap some of the surrounding primordial gas. The eventual accretion of the (now cold) dust into solid bodies, and the separation of the solids from the noncondensable gas would proceed along the path outlined by Urey (1952a, 1954, 1956, 1957a, 1958), Fish et al. (1960), Fowler et al. (1962), or Cameron (1962).

Another opportunity for a brief high-temperature era might occur during contraction of the protosun. The luminosity may have been as much as 10^3 times its present value when the sun had contracted to 10^2 times its present radius (see the paper by A. G. W. Cameron, "Contraction of the sun toward the Main Sequence," in this volume). Regardless of mechanism, an early high-temperature stage may be regarded, if not an essential boundary condition, so at least a desideratum for any theory of the origin of the solar system, inasmuch as it provides a convenient explanation for some properties of the meteorites.

Meteorites representing this hypothetical, primitive material have not been identified with certainty, though several possible candidates have been proposed [Renazzo (Wood, 1962b); Ornans (DuFresne and Anders, 1962a)]. Renazzo, in particular, contains a mineral assemblage that is far removed from chemical equilibrium: chondrules of forsterite (Mg_2SiO_4 nearly free of iron), surrounded by metal rims, and embedded in a carbonaceous matrix containing magnetite (Fe_3O_4) and a very fine-grained silicate. The chondrules and the metal must have formed under strongly reducing conditions at high temperatures, whereas the coexistence of free carbon with the highly oxidized magnetite suggests low-temperature conditions. The presence of glass in the chondrules suggests a fast cooling rate, on a time scale of days or less.

All these properties are difficult to explain in terms of evolution in a meteorite parent body, but agree rather well with those expected for a conglomerate of primitive material formed according to Wood's hypothesis. The presence of iron-rich olivine in some carbonaceous chondrites is harder to understand, since only iron-poor olivine should form in the presence of the cosmic ratio of H_2 to H_2O. This seems to require some special assumptions, such as a partial gas-solid separation at an early stage, and more than one heating and cooling cycle. Although these assumptions are esthetically objectionable because of their complexity, there is no a priori reason why the temperature and composition of the nebula should always have changed monotonically.

The other chondrites may have evolved from this primitive material along several paths. The carbonaceous chondrites could have been produced by the (preterrestrial) action of liquid water. The enstatite chondrites could have been derived from either the primitive material itself, or from the carbonaceous chondrites by strong heating in a closed system, so that neither the trace elements other than mercury nor the noble gases would be lost. Finally, if the ordinary chondrites, too, were derived from the same material, then they must have been processed still more drastically. The primordial noble gases and the trace elements were lost somehow, the silicates were recrystallized until their iron content became uniform, and carbon and its compounds were either lost or consumed by reactions with reducible substances (Fe_3O_4, Fe^{2+}, etc.). Of course, there is no assurance that the ordinary chondrites are lineal descendants of this primitive ancestor. They may have originated from material with a different condensation history and, hence, composition (cf. Section IV,B).

If such a high-temperature stage ever took place, then cometary matter, too, must have passed through it. This raises some new possibilities in regard to the mineral composition of comets. In particular, the presence in comet tails of metal (or magnetite?) spherules, inferred from polarization and scattered light measurements (Liller, 1960), is somewhat easier to understand if at least part of the cometary material had a high-temperature history, even though its final accretion occurred at low temperatures. This view gains further support from the discovery in cosmic dust of metal flakes with amorphous organic attachments. The fall dates of these particles seem to be correlated with several meteor showers of cometary origin (Parkin *et al.*, 1962). Perhaps Herbig's (1961) suggestion that the carbonaceous chondrites were derived from comets should be re-examined in the light of this possibility.

It must be emphasized that the early high-temperature stage does not eliminate the need for a heat source in the meteorite parent bodies. As pointed out in the Introduction, such a heat source is needed to produce the iron meteorites, and to account for the compact textures and pronounced metamorphism of many chondrites (Wood, 1962b). If the meteorites had originated in bodies of lunar size, then either chemical reactions of thermodynamically unstable compounds, or adiabatic compression of gases can be invoked, although some special assumptions are needed in each case. Both processes require growth of lunar-sized objects prior to the dissipation of the solar nebula, a rather narrow range of heating and cooling rates, and a closely timed breakup. On the other hand, if the meteorites are derived from asteroids, none of the above mechanisms is effective, and heating by 0.74×10^6 year Al^{26} seems to be the principal remaining possibility.

C. Aqueous Stage

If the meteorites came from a planet-sized body, then the requirement of an aqueous stage is easy to satisfy. Planets of terrestrial size are able to hold water vapor gravitationally, and can maintain bodies of liquid water, from ponds to oceans. If the meteorites come from the Moon, some ad hoc assumption is required. One such process was recently discussed by Urey (1962b).

For the asteroids, the prospects are bleak: of all the parent bodies discussed, they are least likely to retain liquid water *at their surfaces*, owing to their small size and consequent low escape velocities. But there is a way in which they could retain liquid water in their interiors. If the asteroids were ever heated by an internal heat source (e.g., extinct radioactivity), their interior temperatures would increase with depth. The surface temperature of the body, being controlled by the amount of solar radiation reaching it, might be around 100–200°K. Further inward, the temperature would rise until the melting point of ice was reached. Liquid water could exist in this zone, down to a depth where the boiling point at the prevailing pressure was reached (DuFresne and Anders, 1962a; Anders, 1963). At a central temperature of 1900°K, some 5% of the volume of the body will contain liquid water.

Of course, the water will not last forever. Above the zone of liquid water, there will be a permafrost zone (Gold, 1961). This permafrost zone can serve to retain an "internal atmosphere" within the meteorite parent body, and may have played a role in the retention of primordial noble gases (DuFresne and Anders, 1962a,b). Ice from this zone will evaporate at a rate determined by its vapor pressure (Watson *et al.*, 1961). The vapor pressure depends on the temperature, which, in turn, depends mainly on the distance from the sun. For an asteroid of 100 km radius, with an initial water content of 10%, these times range from 2×10^6 years to more than 10^{10} years, depending on the distance from the sun. These times are certainly long enough to allow the formation of the characteristic minerals.

III. Primordial Noble Gases

More than from their usefulness in the identification of primitive matter, primordial noble gases in meteorites also shed some light on the separation of solids and gases that must have occurred at some time during the formation of the solar system.

About twenty meteorites, including representatives of all major classes, are known that contain substantial amounts of primordial noble gases. Some of these meteorites (irons and achondrites) are several steps removed from primitive matter, and must have undergone extensive chemical processing in the meteorite parent bodies before the gases were incorporated somehow in their present locations. This implies that the meteorite parent bodies were able to store appreciable amounts of noble gases over extended periods, perhaps in an "internal atmosphere" (DuFresne and Anders, 1962b; Anders, 1962). Other meteorites, such as the carbonaceous chondrites, may have retained their gases in the sites in which they were originally trapped from the nebula, although they, too, may have released and reabsorbed the gases during residence in the parent body. No convincing argument can be made for the remaining meteorites (enstatite chondrites and some brecciated ordinary chondrites), but it seems likely that the final trapping occurred in the parent bodies as well, possibly under shock conditions (Fredriksson, 1962).

In the majority of cases, the original distribution seems to have been altered by diffusion losses at some later stage of the meteorites' history. These effects should be minimal for meteorites with high He^4 content, since He diffuses more readily than Ne and the heavier noble gases. Data for 4 meteorites with the highest He^4 content are shown in Fig. 3. For ease of comparison, the depletion factors (defined as the ratio of observed to "cosmic" abundance) are plotted against mass number. Data for the Earth and the enstatite chondrite Abee have also been included.

In the case of the earth, Suess (1949) drew attention to the fact that Kr and Xe had virtually the same depletion factor of $\sim 10^7$, whereas Ar

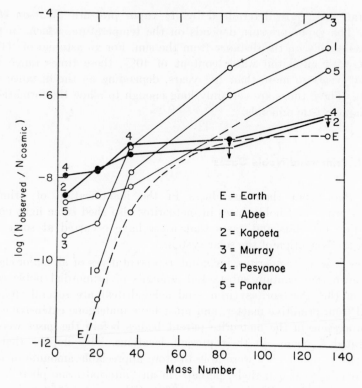

FIG. 3. Depletion factors for noble gases in meteorites and the earth (for references, see Table III). Solid circles, achondrites; open circles, chondrites. Upper limits are denoted by horizontal bars. The broken line indicates Suess' fractionation function [Eq. (1)].

and particularly Ne were depleted by larger factors. The data could be represented by the equation[1]

$$- \log (N_{ter}/N_{cos}) = 10 \exp (- 0.045 \, M/m_1) + 7.1 \qquad (1)$$

which is identical in form to the equation for mass fractionation during escape of a gas from a gravitational field

$$- \ln (N_t/N_0) = tA \exp (- Mgr/RT) \qquad (2)$$

(N_{ter} = terrestrial abundance; N_{cos} = "cosmic" abundance; N_0 = initial abundance; N_t = abundance at time t; M = molecular weight; m_1 =

---

[1] Better agreement with the Suess and Urey (1956) abundances is obtained by changing the constant in Eq. (1) from 7.1 to 6.9. This change has been made in Fig. 3.

atomic weight unit; A = constant; g = gravitational acceleration in escape layer; r = distance of escape layer from center of gravity; R = gas constant; T = temperature).

For gases of high M, the fractionation factor in Eq. (1) approaches the asymptotic value of $10^{-7.1}$. Suess therefore suggested that the gas loss from the earth took place in two stages: first, a general depletion (without mass fractionation) to $10^{-7.1}$ the initial value, followed by a second stage involving mass fractionation. He pointed out, however, that the small value of the exponent $Mgr/RT = 0.045\ M/m_1$ presented some difficulties. With the present value for the earth's gravitational acceleration, no escape of neon, let alone heavier gases, is possible—even assuming the extreme conditions of T = 3000°K and r = 15,000 km. Consequently, Suess argued that the escape occurred either during a planetesimal stage preceding the formation of the earth, or during an era when the earth's period of rotation was so short that centrifugal force largely offset the gravitational force in the upper atmosphere.

This mechanism may or may not be valid for the Earth, but it is evident from Fig. 3 that most of the meteoritic data do not fit an exponential fractionation function of the form of Eq. (1). Two basic patterns seem to be present. The two achondrites, Kapoeta and Pesyanoe, show virtually no fractionation from Ar to Xe, if allowance is made for the fact that the Kr and Xe points are only upper limits. The lighter gases, He and Ne, are fractionated slightly, but, as argued below, the depletion factors show a much smaller mass dependence than expected for gravitational fractionation. The three chondrites show a progressively smaller depletion of the heavier noble gases, in qualitative accord with Eq. (1). But the depletion factors for the lighter gases are grossly inconsistent with a fractionation mechanism dependent on mass alone. Any such function with an exponent large enough to reproduce the observed fractionation of neon relative to xenon must, by necessity, predict a very large depletion of helium. For example, Eq. (1) predicts a depletion of He relative to Ne by a factor of 2×10^4. The observed depletion in chondrites amounts to less than a factor of two in 2 out of 3 cases—Murray and Pantar. The third chondrite, Abee, shows a much greater depletion, consistent with gravitational fractionation, but it is not certain that the He was not lost at a late stage.

The isotopic ratios also do not agree with the expected values for gravitational fractionation (Table III). Geiss (1957) has used Eq. (1) to calculate the neon and argon isotopic composition in primordial matter from the terrestrial isotropic ratios. With the exception of Goalpara, the observed meteoritic Ar^{36}/Ar^{38} ratios in Table III are constant to $\sim5\%$, and are exceedingly close to the atmospheric value of 5.35, much below the

TABLE III

PRIMORDIAL NOBLE GASES IN METEORITES

Meteorite	Class	Ne^{20} (10^{-8} cc STP/gm)	Ne^{20}/Ar^{36}	Ne^{20}/Ne^{22}	Ar^{36}/Ar^{38}	Ref.[a]
Novo Urei	Ureilite	<1.3	<0.0055		5.36	a
Goalpara	Ureilite	<1.0	<0.026		5.88	a
Lancé	Carbonaceous chondrite	3.3	0.019		5.36	a
Felix	Carbonaceous chondrite	5.6	0.031		5.40	a
Felix	Carbonaceous chondrite	4		5.5	5.5	b
Mighei	Carbonaceous chondrite	12	0.20	8.3	5.4	b
Ivuna	Carbonaceous chondrite	20.9	0.22	9.8	5.37	a
Cold Bokkeveld	Carbonaceous chondrite	10.0	0.23	9.0	5.5	b
Abee	Enstatite chondrite	6.3	0.25	9.3	5.50	a, b
Murray	Carbonaceous chondrite	53.8	0.39	10.6	5.37	a
Murray	Carbonaceous chondrite	39.7	0.58	9.7	5.5	b
Murray	Carbonaceous chondrite	63.2	0.83	9.2	5.47	c
Orgueil	Carbonaceous chondrite	46.4	0.69	11	5.6	b
Mokoia	Carbonaceous chondrite	309	9.1	13.2	5.39	a
Pantar (dark)	Veined chondrite	394	16	12.4	5.2	d, e
		(178)		(11.6)		e
Pesyanoe	Aubrite	2150	11.9	12.2	5.46	a, f
Pesyanoe	Aubrite	2060	15	12.5	5.4	b
Kapoeta	Achondrite	2220	24	13.5	5.2	b
Atmosphere			0.52	10.2	5.35	
"Cosmos"			61.4	23.0	7.87	g

[a] REFERENCES

a. Stauffer (1961)
b. Zähringer (1962)
c. Reynolds (1960b)
d. König et al. (1961)
e. Reynolds et al. (1962)
f. Gerling and Levskii (1956)
g. Suess and Urey (1956)

calculated primordial value of 7.87. In the case of neon, the ratio is more variable, but the agreement with the calculated primordial value is worse, if anything.

Nevertheless, it is of interest that the meteorites with Ne^{20}/Ar^{38} ratios closest to the "cosmic" value of 61 also happen to have the highest Ne^{20}/Ne^{22} ratios (Fig. 4). Evidently, some mass fractionation did take place during the loss of neon. The problem is, to find a process that would give the observed isotopic fractionation of neon, without, at the same time, producing large elemental fractionations between Ne and He.

One such process is diffusion. For a gas trapped in a crystal grain of radius a, the rate of escape depends on the diffusion parameter D/a^2, where D, the diffusion coefficient, is given by

$$D = D_0 \exp(-Q/RT) \tag{3}$$

(Q = activation energy; D_0 = a constant). Both Q and D_0 vary from one mineral and one gas to another, the heavier gases and more densely packed minerals generally having larger values of Q. It is seen from Eq.

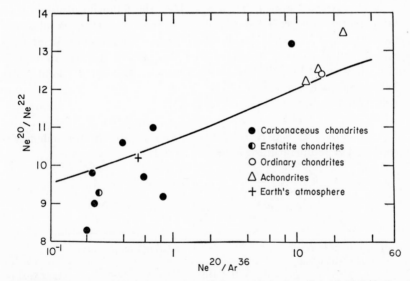

Fig. 4. Isotopic composition of primordial neon as a function of Ne^{20}/Ar^{36} ratio [Adapted from Zähringer (1962)]. The Ne^{20}/Ne^{22} decreases with the Ne^{20}/Ar^{36} ratio, indicating that some isotopic fractionation took place during the elemental fractionation of Ne and Ar. The solid curve shows the isotopic fractionation expected during diffusion, assuming no argon loss, and a $M^{-\frac{1}{2}}$ dependence of the diffusion coefficient (Zähringer, 1962). Better agreement with the data would have been obtained if some Ar loss had been assumed for the meteorites on the left.

(3) that the fractionation between two gases will be strongly temperature-dependent, any differences in D being accentuated at low temperatures. The diffusion mechanism can thus be invoked to account for almost any observed elemental fractionation, large or small, particularly if the gases are unevenly distributed among several minerals differing in retentivity and grain size.

Diffusion will also result in isotopic fractionations, since both D_0 and Q are mass-dependent. Zähringer (1962) suggested, citing the work of Lazarus (1960), that D should be proportional to $M^{-\frac{1}{2}}$. Assuming an initially uniform distribution of gas in spherical grains of radius a, the fraction f lost during time t is found to be

$$f = 1 - \sum_{n=1}^{\infty} \frac{6}{n^2\pi^2} \exp\left[- \frac{n^2\pi^2 D(M) t}{a^2} \right] \tag{4}$$

which simplifies to

$$f = \frac{6}{\pi^2} \exp\left[- \frac{\pi^2 D(M) t}{a^2} \right] \tag{5}$$

if f is large (>0.85). Setting $D(M) \propto M^{-\frac{1}{2}}$, the following isotopic fractionation factors are predicted (Table IV). It is seen that the observed constancy of $\pm 5\%$ in the Ar^{36}/Ar^{38} ratio implies a retention of at least 10% of the initial argon, whereas the variation in Ne^{20}/Ne^{22} ratio ($\sim 30\%$) implies a loss of all but 0.1% of the initial neon content. As pointed out by Zähringer, such variations in the degree of retention would result if the diffusion constants of Ne and Ar differed by as little as a factor of 4. The experimentally observed ratios D_{Ne}/D_{Ar} range from 3 for a carbonaceous chondrite at $950°K$ (Stauffer, 1961) to 10^4 for the achondrite Kapoeta at low temperatures (Zähringer, 1962).

TABLE IV

ISOTOPIC FRACTIONATION BY DIFFUSION
(From Zähringer, 1962)

Fraction of heavy isotope remaining (%)	Relative isotopic ratio		
	He^3/Hd^4	Ne^{20}/Ne^{22}	Ar^{36}/Ar^{38}
100	1	1	1
10	0.76	0.91	0.95
1	0.53	0.81	0.90
0.1	0.37	0.72	0.84
0.01	0.22	0.63	—

To account for the lack of elemental fractionation between Ne and He, some additional assumption is required. If the gases were initially distributed between two types of sites differing in retentivity, the lighter gases might be largely lost from one type of site, while being retained in their original proportions in the other. In fact, even a difference in grain size might lead to much the same result (Zähringer, 1962). The grain radius enters the diffusion parameter D/a^2 to the inverse second power, so that a doubling of the grain size is equivalent to a reduction in the diffusion constant by a factor of 4, which, as mentioned above, would cause a one hundred-fold increase in the fraction of gas retained. Neither of these assumptions seems particularly contrived, and it thus appears that the diffusion mechanism is able to account for all the elemental and isotopic frastionations observed in the meteorites and the earth.

Suess (1962) has pointed out that the meteoritic data in Fig. 3 could still be explained in terms of his model (loss of all but $\sim 10^{-7}$ of the initial gas by hydrodynamic flow, followed by gravitational fractionation of the remainder), if a small amount of unfractionated gas were retained or added. By this view, most of the atmospheric and meteoritic neon is unfractionated, and is close to primordial neon in isotopic composition. Then the "primordial" Ne^{20}/Ne^{22} ratio calculated from Eq. (1) has no quantitative significance, and its disagreement with the observed values does not rule out gravitational fractionation. For argon, however, the unfractionated component should be negligible, yet an Ar^{36}/Ar^{38} ratio virtually identical to the terrestrial value is found in meteorites differing greatly in absolute and relative noble gas contents, including the two achondrites. This fact is difficult to reconcile with gravitational fractionation, although the possibility cannot be ruled out entirely for the terrestrial gases, at least. However, the diffusion mechanism proposed for the meteorites is also capable of accounting for the terrestrial fractionations. Hence the constraint that solid objects of appreciable size ($r >$ 1000 km) must have accreted *before* the dissipation of the gases, no longer seems binding.

Another possibility to be considered is that the Earth's noble gases may be of secondary origin. Urey (1952a,b) suggested that an appreciable addition to the Earth's noble gas inventory might have been made by cometary material, whereas Cameron (1962) proposed that much of the Earth's xenon was of solar origin. Neither of these suggestions is incompatible with the conclusion reached above: that noble gas fractionation by diffusion appears to be an adequate explanation for both the meteoritic and terrestrial data.

Unfortunately, the flexibility of the diffusion mechanism, which was helpful in accounting for a complicated set of data, also makes it difficult to deduce an unambiguous history from these data. One observation of fundamental importance is the presence of noble gases in nearly cosmic proportions in the two achondrites. This seems to imply that the initial trapping of the gas by solid particles occurred at an early stage, prior to any elemental fractionation of the individual gases. The further accretion of the particles to larger bodies must have occurred under low-temperature conditions, to avoid preferential loss of the lighter gases. This places a limit the order of 1 km/sec on the impact velocity of the accreting particles, and seems to suggest that the sun did not attain its high-luminosity stage until the meteoritic matter had accreted to thermally insulated planetesimals. These planetesimals may have been either the building blocks of the meteorite parent bodies, or the parent bodies themselves. After accretion of the meteorite parent bodies, the gases were stored without loss in some reservoir, while the primitive matter melted and differentiated into achondrites.

It is not quite clear how the gases were reintroduced into the meteorites from this reservoir, but it seems likely that shock was involved in some manner. Kapoeta consists of two distinct fractions, which, though identical in chemical composition, differ in color and primordial gas content (Signer and Suess, 1962; Fredriksson and Keil, 1963). Only the dark fraction, which is also rich in glass, contains primordial gases. It appears that the differences between the two fractions were produced by shock, and this process may also have introduced the noble gases. For Pesyanoe, a variety of other mechanisms have been proposed (DuFresne and Anders, 1962b), but it is not unlikely that shock was in fact responsible.

The evidence from chondrites is more ambiguous. It is certainly striking that the curves for all three chondrites in Fig. 3 agree so well in the region Ar–Xe, any differences being confined to the lighter gases. Yet the three meteorites differ drastically in their chemical and thermal histories, belonging, as they do, to the three principal subclasses of chondrites (see Section II). The ordinary chondrite Pantar, which is farthest removed from primordial matter, shows the same nonuniform distribution of noble gases between two fractions as does Kapoeta, and it is again probable that the gases were introduced in their present locations by shock. This makes it necessary to assume a reservoir (perhaps an "internal atmosphere") where the gases were stored before their final incorporation in Pantar. Primordial gases are also found in small amounts in nearly all ordinary chondrites (Geiss and Hess, 1958; Zähringer, 1962), and, in substantially greater amounts, in the carbonaceous and enstatite chondrites.

It is thus necessary to assume that the meteorites either retained some of their initial endowment of primordial gases, or that they all experienced some process that reintroduced the gases from a reservoir. Very little is known about the physical location of the gases in these types of meteorites, and it is hence not possible to decide between these alternatives.

It is also not clear whether the gases in the chondrites were fractionated in the parent body or in the nebula. The similarity of the Ar–Xe fractionation may be taken to indicate either a common gas reservoir in the parent body, or a common fractionation history of the primitive matter before accretion. The fractionation of the He and Ne could have occurred at a later stage in either case.

If the initial trapping of the gases had occurred under anything like equilibrium conditions, then the primordial gas content of primitive dust (as approximated by the present gas content of meteorites) might provide a crude lower limit to the ambient gas pressure at time of trapping. Inasmuch as the ordinary chondrites are by far the most abundant class of meteorites, their average primordial gas content should give a conservative lower limit to the gas content of primordial dust (Table V).

TABLE V

AVERAGE PRIMORDIAL GAS CONTENTS OF METEORITES

Meteorite class	Primordial gas content $(10^{-8}$ cc STP/gm)		Calculated partial pressure of H^2 in gas phase atmosphere	
	Ar^{36}	Xe^{132}	From Ar^{36}	From Xe^{132}
Ordinary chondrites	2.9	0.034	7.4	1.2×10^4
Carbonaceous chondrites	85	0.81	220	2.9×10^5
Enstatite chondrites	26	0.067	68	2.4×10^4
Weighted average of all chondrites	6.9	0.063	18	2.2×10^4
Achondrites	23	?	59	?

Somewhat higher values are obtained for the other classes, and for a weighted average of the three subclasses of chondrites. If it is now assumed that the gases were dissolved in the silicate phase of the dust under conditions where Henry's law was obeyed, the equilibrium partial pressures in the gas phase can be calculated. Assuming a gas phase of primordial composition, and a solubility in silicates of all noble gases equal to that of He at $1500°-2000°C$ [2.84×10^{-3} cc STP/gm at 1 atm pressure (Gerling and Levskii, 1956)], one obtains the following partial pressures of H_2 (the most abundant gas) in the hypothetical gas phase from which the meteorite gases were trapped (Columns 4 and 5, Table V).

These pressures are surprisingly high, particularly those calculated from the xenon content. Even the lowest of these are attained in current models of the protosun only at distances well within the orbit of Mercury (Cameron: "Contraction of the Sun toward the Main Sequence," in this volume). Urey's (1962a) photolunar objects do provide pressures of the required order, but it is not certain whether they would also furnish suitable conditions for the development of other properties of the meteorites. It seems that one or several further assumptions will have to be made to account for the primordial gases in chondrites.

(1) Trapping in silicates at high temperatures was not the principal mechanism.

(2) Adsorption by the low-temperature condensate (Wood, 1962a) may have played an important role, and would explain the tendency of noble gases to occur in meteorites rich in carbon or carbon compounds. Some enrichment of the heavier gases would occur under these conditions.

(3) Trapping by gas hydrates may have been important (Miller, 1961). This mechanism, too, would favor the heavier gases.

(4) After initial trapping in the primary condensates, the gases may have been selectively lost by reheating in the very early stages of the accretion process. The degree of loss would vary with the size of the accreting objects. Very complex fractionation patterns might result if the accretion of primitive matter to the meteorite parent bodies proceeded through planetesimals of intermediate size (Cameron, 1962; Fowler *et al.*, 1962).

Thus it is difficult to establish the time and the circumstances of the initial gas-solid separation. The evidence from achondrites suggests nonselective trapping, presumably at an early stage. The evidence from chondrites, on the other hand, suggests selective trapping under circumstances favoring the enrichment of the heavier gases, or selective losses leading to the same result. No simple model can satisfy both these conditions, and it is thus necessary to assume a more complicated series of events. It can only be said that the gases were still present in cosmic proportions at the time of condensation of the first solid particles, and that they were dispersed by the time the earth had grown to a size large enough to hold the gases gravitationally. This conclusion is not new.

IV. Chemical Fractionations in Chondrites

The various subgroups of chondrites show certain compositional variations among themselves. If they were all derived from a single pool of primordial matter of initially uniform composition, each compositional difference must indicate some chemical fractionation process. A priori, it is not possible to decide whether a given fractionation took place in the nebula or in the parent body. But in some cases, evidence exists that favors one or the other of these alternatives.

A. Metal-Silicate Fractionation

In absolute terms, the largest such fractionation is that between iron and silicon. Urey and Craig (1953) drew attention to the fact that the chondrites fell into two groups (Fig. 5), differing in total Fe content (22 and 28%) and hence Fe/Si ratio (0.60 and 0.85). Later, Urey (1959) pointed out that the density of the moon (3.38–3.41 at low temperature and pressure) was somewhat lower than that of the chondrites of the low-iron group (3.51). Either the moon had the same low iron content as the L-group chondrites, and a water content of several percent, which

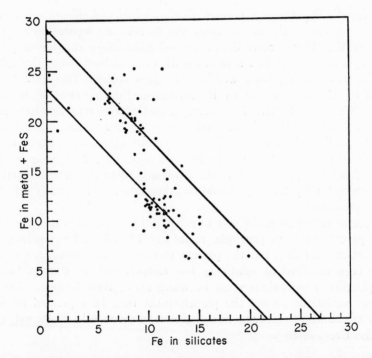

FIG. 5. Distribution of iron between oxidized (silicate) and reduced (metal + troilite) phases in chondrites (Urey and Craig, 1953). Two groups appear to be present, differing in degree of oxidation, and total iron content. Two lines of constant iron content are shown.

would account for the lower density, or else its iron content was lower still. Previously, Urey (1952a, 1957a) had noted that the variable density of the terrestrial planets could be attributed to differences in the proportions of iron and silicon.

All these lines of evidence point to a fractionation between iron and silicon, presumably as metal and silicate, respectively. Urey has suggested two such processes:

(1) Heating of asteroidal-sized planetesimals, accreted from primordial dust in a reducing atmosphere. Under these conditions, silicates would be volatilized preferentially, whereas the denser metal would sink to the interior (Urey, 1952a).

(2) Production of metal and silicates in "primary" objects of lunar size, followed by breakup into minute fragments. The brittler silicates are expected to break into smaller and less dense fragments which would be lost preferentially with the gas during the dissipation of the nebula (Urey, 1956).

If Wood's hypothesis is correct, so that metal and silicate grains were already present in the nebula immediately after its separation from the sun (Section II,B), then Urey's second mechanism can be simplified. These particles could be fractionated directly, without going through an interim period of residence within lunar-sized objects. This fractionation might be enhanced further by the ferromagnetic properties of the metal grains (Cameron, 1959b). Moreover, magnetic forces may also have aided in the accretion of the micron-sized dust to larger aggregates. Most of the silicate particles in the Orgueil carbonaceous chondrite contain minute inclusions of magnetite, and similar inclusions have been seen in chondrules from Kaba (Sztrókay *et al.*, 1961) and other chondrites (Fredriksson, 1962). This possibility should be taken into account in any estimates of accretion rates.

It seems rather more difficult to achieve this fractionation in the meteorite parent body. In principle, metal can be removed by melting and gravitational settling, but the present textures of the chondrites seem to have been acquired at relatively low temperatures so that additional, complicating assumptions must be made about their history. Also, the density variations among the planets must then be explained by some other mechanism [e.g., reduction of silicon to the metal (Ringwood, 1959; see also Urey, 1960)].

B. Trace Element Abundances

As already mentioned in Section II,B, the chalcophile trace elements (Bi, Cd, Hg, I, In, Pb, Sb, Te, and Tl) seem to have been fractionated much more severely in chondrites than iron, depletion factors of up to 1000 having been observed (Fig. 1). It is not immediately obvious whether this fractionation occurred in the nebula or the parent body. The most promising approach seems to be to find some common property of these elements that distinguishes them from other unfractionated trace elements, and then to look for a mechanism that would produce a fractionation based on this property.

Cursory inspection might suggest volatility as a common characteristic, but closer examination reveals several inconsistencies: Bi and Tl are depleted more strongly than the relatively volatile Hg and I, for example. A better correlation is found with geochemical character. As already pointed out by Suess (1947) on the basis of the early data of Goldschmidt (1937), most of these "deficient" elements are chalcophile. Still another trend may be noted in Fig. 6: for the strongly depleted elements on the left, the boiling points are higher than the decomposition temperatures of the sulfides, whereas the reverse seems to be true for the less strongly depleted elements on the right. The highly volatile elements Hg, Cd, and

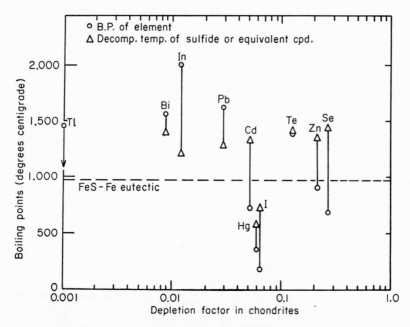

Fig. 6. Boiling points of chalcophile elements and their compounds. The depletion of these elements in ordinary chondrites is not a simple function of volatility. The most strongly depleted elements Tl, Bi, and In have boiling points higher than the decomposition temperature of their sulfides. The reverse seems to be true for the less strongly depleted elements Se, Te, and Zn on the right. The elements of very high volatility (Cd, Hg, and I) show an intermediate degree of depletion.

I seem to occupy an intermediate position, and some ad hoc assumption may be required in their case. The position of Pb is uncertain, as the estimates of the cosmic abundance diverge widely [0.47 (Suess and Urey, 1956); 22 (Cameron, 1959a)]. In this graph, the abundance of Pb in carbonaceous chondrites was assumed to be equal to the cosmic abundance.

On the basis of these data, Fish *et al.* (1960) and Anders and Goles (1961) proposed a cyclic process that might account for the observed depletion. In an internally heated asteroid, the first major phase to melt will be the FeS–Fe eutectic (M.P. 1260°K). Owing to its high density, it will flow toward the center, extracting chalcophile elements from the chondritic mantle rock. In its flow toward the core, the melt will experience higher and higher temperatures, causing the trace element sulfides to decompose. The more volatile elements will return to the mantle, canceling, in part, the original depletion, whereas the less volatile ones (Bi, Tl) will reach the core, and become concentrated in a sulfide-phosphide zone.

This model has its weaknesses (Anders and Goles, 1961), and it may well be that the fractionation, while being based on the properties displayed in Fig. 6, took place in an altogether different setting, perhaps even in the solar nebula. As mentioned in Section II,B, it is by no means certain that all meteorites were derived from a single type of ancestral material. It is perhaps significant that both subclasses that have retained chalcophile trace elements in normal abundances (the carbonaceous and enstatite chondrites) also contain free carbon and primordial noble gases, while the carbonaceous chondrites contain water and organic compounds as well. It may be that these gross differences in composition, which set them apart from the ordinary chondrites, reflect differences in condensation or accretion conditions. Perhaps the ancestral material of the ordinary chondrites condensed at high temperatures and low pressures, where the trace elements are volatile, or was reheated before accretion so that these substances were lost. Although it is esthetically objectionable to have more than one set of condensation conditions, this possibility cannot be ruled out on factual grounds at present. It is also possible that some other property was actually of importance in the fractionation. For example, it can be seen from Vogel's (1961) survey of the ternary phase diagrams of 28 metals with iron and sulfur, that all 3 "deficient" elements represented in his study (Bi, Pb, and Tl) have two characteristics in common. Their sulfides are reduced to the metal by free iron, and the metals are immiscible with metallic iron. These properties set them apart from all other elements included in this study (except Ag, for which the degree of depletion in chondrites is not known, however). It may well be that the fractionation was actually based on these properties, be it in the parent body or in the nebula. At present, however, this part of the record remains undeciphered.

V. Extinct Radioactivity and General Isotopic Anomalies

One of the most significant clues to the early history of the solar system is extinct radioactivity. Brown (1947) predicted that the decay products of such radionuclides (with half-lives 10^6–10^8 years) might be detectable in the meteorites if they had formed shortly after a nucleogenetic event. After several unsuccessful searches [Wasserburg and Hayden (1955); Reynolds and Lipson (1957); see Kohman (1956) for a review], Reynolds (1960a) at last detected a 50% enrichment of Xe^{129} in the Richardton chondrite. This enrichment was probably due to the one-time presence in the meteorite of 16.4×10^6 year I^{129}.

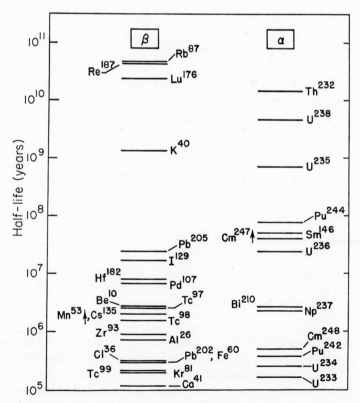

FIG. 7. Long-lived natural radioactivities [Adapted from Kohman (1956)]. Arrows indicate lower limits to the half-life.

Not all of the 15 or so radioactivities in the half-life range 10^6 to 10^8 years (Fig. 7) are likely to be recognized in meteorites by way of their decay products. To leave detectable traces, an extinct radioactivity must have a high initial abundance, and a large geochemical fractionation factor from its decay product. It is also essential that the decay product have at least one nonradiogenic isotope, so that an isotopic rather than merely a chemical enrichment results. If these criteria are applied to the radionuclides in Fig. 7, only six remain:

$$
\begin{array}{lll}
(1) & \mathrm{Pu}^{244}\ \Big\{ &
\begin{array}{l}
\xrightarrow[\substack{76\ \text{m.y.}}]{\substack{\alpha,\ 99.7\%}} \mathrm{Th}^{232} \\[1em]
\xrightarrow[\substack{\ }]{\substack{\text{S.F.},\ 0.3\%}} \mathrm{Xe}^{136}\ (\sim 6\%),\ \text{etc.}
\end{array}
\end{array}
$$

$$(2) \quad \mathrm{Cm}^{247} \xrightarrow[\substack{\geq 40\ \text{m.y.}}]{\substack{\alpha}} \mathrm{U}^{235}$$

$$(3) \quad \mathrm{Pb}^{205} \xrightarrow[\substack{\sim 24\ \text{m.y.}}]{\substack{\text{E.C.}}} \mathrm{Tl}^{205}$$

$$(4) \quad \mathrm{I}^{129} \xrightarrow[\substack{16.4\ \text{m.y.}}]{\substack{\beta^-}} \mathrm{Xe}^{129}$$

$$(5) \quad \mathrm{Hf}^{182} \xrightarrow[\substack{8\ \text{m.y.}}]{\substack{\beta^-}} \mathrm{W}^{182}$$

$$(6) \quad \mathrm{Pd}^{107} \xrightarrow[\substack{6.8\ \text{m.y.}}]{\substack{\beta^-}} \mathrm{Ag}^{107}$$

A. Chronology of the Early Solar System

The most important information that can be obtained from extinct radioactivity is a relative age scale for meteorites, and, hopefully, planets and satellites. The following assumptions are made in the derivation of such an age scale.

(1) At some time in the past the extinct radionuclide X^A was synthesized either in the Galaxy or in the solar nebula. (This nuclide decays with a mean life τ to the stable nuclide Y^A.)

(2) At some later time t_0 production of X^A ceased abruptly, and unsupported decay began. The initial amounts at t_0 were X_0^A and Y_0^A.

(3) After the formation of solid objects, chemical fractionations between elements X and Y set in. If the last such fractionation occurred at time t, and the object remained a closed system thereafter, the one-time abundance of X^A can be related to the present-day abundance of Y^A. Defining $\Delta t_{XY} \equiv t - t_0$, and using the subscripts r = radiogenic and p = present, we write:

$$X_t{}^A = X_0{}^A \exp - (\Delta t_{XY}/\tau) = Y_{r,p}^A = Y_p{}^A - Y_0{}^A - Y_{r,t}^A \qquad (6)$$

For convenience, the abundances can be normalized to the stable, non-radiogenic isotopes X^B and Y^C

$$\frac{X_t{}^A}{Y^C} = \frac{X_0{}^A}{X^B} \cdot \frac{X^B}{Y^C} \exp - (\Delta t_{XY}/\tau) = \frac{Y_{r,p}^A}{Y^C} = \frac{Y_p{}^A - Y_t{}^A}{Y^C} \qquad (7)$$

where

$$Y_t{}^A = Y_0{}^A + Y_{r,t}^A$$

Of course, this involves the tacit assumption that the solar nebula was isotopically homogeneous, and that no appreciable isotopic fractionations took place (other than those caused by radioactive decay).

In principle, this equation can be used to calculate Δt_{XY} [= "decay interval" (Goles and Anders, 1961), or "formation interval" (Cameron, 1962)], but there are two practical difficulties in the application of this method. The amount of X^A at t_0 (i.e., $X_0{}^A/X^B$) and the isotopic composition of Y at time t (specifically, $Y_t{}^A/Y^C$) must be known. The latter can hardly ever be determined exactly, since it requires, for every object to be dated, another object that separated from the solar nebula at the identical time t, with so high a ratio of Y to X that subsequent decay of X^A did not change the isotopic composition of Y appreciably. Under favorable circumstances (e.g., when $X_0{}^A/Y_0{}^A$ is small, and $X_t{}^A/Y_t{}^A$ is large), even a crude approximation of $Y_t{}^A/Y^C$ will suffice, but when the isotopic anomaly is small, the uncertainties become quite large. To stress the distinction between $Y_0{}^A/Y^C$, which may be regarded constant for the entire solar system,[2] and $Y_t{}^A/Y^C$, which varies with t, we shall use the terms "primordial" and "primeval" for these two quantities.

The amount of the extinct radionuclide present at t depends on the model assumed for nucleosynthesis. It is generally agreed that the elements were continuously synthesized in the Galaxy (Burbidge and co-workers, 1957). If the further assumption is made that the rate of synthesis has remained constant with time (Wasserburg et al., 1960), the amount

---

[2] Some doubts have now arisen concerning the validity of this assumption (Section V, B).

of a stable nuclide X^B synthesized during time T (defined as the duration of nucleosynthesis prior to the formation of the solar system) equals

$$X^B = K_B T$$

where K_B is the production rate of X^B. For a radioactive nuclide X^A, the corresponding equation is

$$X^A = K_A \tau [1 - \exp(- T/\tau)]$$

In the special case of an extinct radionuclide with $\tau \ll T$, this equation simplifies to

$$X^A \approx K_A \tau \qquad (\text{for } \tau \ll T).$$

Hence the ratio X_0^A/X^B in Eq. (7) equals

$$X_0^A/X^B = (K_A/K_B) \cdot (\tau/T) \tag{8}$$

and

$$\frac{Y_p^A - Y_t^A}{Y^C} = \frac{K_A}{K_B} \cdot \frac{X^B}{Y^C} \cdot \frac{\tau}{T} \cdot \exp\left(\frac{\Delta t_{XY}}{\tau}\right) \tag{9}$$

Solving for Δt_{XY}, we obtain:

$$\Delta t_{XY} = \tau \ln \left(\frac{Y^C}{Y_p^A - Y_t^A} \cdot \frac{K^A}{K_B} \cdot \frac{X^B}{Y^C} \cdot \frac{\tau}{T} \right) \tag{10}$$

This model may be an oversimplification inasmuch as the rate of nucleosynthesis can hardly have been constant over the lifetime of the Galaxy. It seems likely that the rate declined with time, as more and more matter became locked up in small and slowly-evolving stars. To allow for this effect, Kohman (1961) proposed inclusion of another negative exponential term in Eq. (9), whereas Cameron (1962) assumed a more complicated model of galactic history. However, for the construction of a *relative* age scale the model of Wasserburg *et al.* is quite adequate, as it provides a self-consistent set of Δt's for each extinct radionuclide. From the degree of agreement of these sets of Δt's one can infer the shortcomings of the model, and the modifications required to bring the Δt's into accord.

1. Iodine–129

The β^- emitter iodine–129 is the extinct radionuclide *par excellence*. Its half-life, 16.4×10^6 years (Kohman, 1961), lies in a convenient range; its abundance is easy to estimate, and its decay product, Xe^{129}, should be easy to detect even at low levels, since the meteorites (and the Earth) seem to have retained very little primordial xenon. Table VI lists Xe^{129}

TABLE VI

I^{129}–Xe^{129} Decay Intervals

Object	Class	Xe^{129}/Xe^{130}	Xenon content (10^{-11} cc STP/gm) Total	Xe$_r^{129}$	I^{127} ppb	Δt (10^6 y)	Ref.[b]
Abee[a]	Enstatite chondrite	15.2	730	430	145	63	b, d, i
Indarch	Enstatite chondrite	19.1	650	250	270	91	b, g
Indarch	Enstatite chondrite		470	210	270	95	b, i
St. Marks[a]	Enstatite chondrite	20.0	360	170	70	68	b, d, i
Bruderheim	Chondrite	7.37	104	3.6	16	123	a, b
Richardton	Chondrite	8.99	104	10	28	113	b, e
Murray	Carbonaceous chondrite	6.48	4300	≤22	230	≥144	b, f
Sardis troilite	Iron	8.54	42	3.3	3600	254	b, h
Atmosphere		6.49	65	(<17)	(65)	≥170	c

[a] For these meteorites, Xe$_r^{129}$ was obtained from Zähringer's Xe^{129}/Xe^{132} and Xe^{132} data, subtracting the atmospheric Xe^{129}/Xe^{132} ratio. The Xe^{129}/Xe^{130} ratio measured by Jeffrey et al. is not quite consistent with these figures, owing to differences in normalization and in the contamination level.

[b] References

a. Clarke and Thode (1961)
b. Goles and Anders (1960, 1962)
c. Goles and Anders (1961)
d. Jeffery and Reynolds (1961a)
e. Reynolds (1960a)
f. Reynolds (1960b)
g. Reynolds (1960c)
h. Reynolds et al. (1962)
i. Zähringer (1962)

contents of meteorites in which both the xenon and iodine have been determined.

On the basis of their xenon content, the meteorites fall into three classes. The "ordinary" (bronzite and hypersthene) chondrites have low xenon contents and zero to moderate Xe^{129} enrichment. The enstatite chondrites have intermediate xenon contents and very large Xe^{129} anomalies. Finally, the carbonaceous chondrites have very large xenon contents with only a slight, if any, Xe^{129} enrichment. The amount of *radiogenic* Xe^{129} in each meteorite is difficult to determine unambiguously. The composition of primeval xenon is not known and atmospheric xenon is therefore used to correct the observed mass spectrum for nonradiogenic Xe^{129}.[3] This practice is questionable in itself, but it also introduces a further ambiguity. The mass spectra of meteoritic and terrestrial xenon are incongruent at all mass numbers, not just at mass 129. Hence the apparent amount of radiogenic Xe^{129} varies with the choice of stable isotope Y^C used in the normalization. These points are more fully discussed elsewhere (Anders, 1962). In the present paper, Xe^{130} is used for normalization (Kuroda, 1960).

Assuming[4] that the Xe^{129} anomaly arose from the *in situ* decay of I^{129}, one can calculate I^{129}–Xe^{129} decay intervals for those meteorites whose xenon and iodine contents are known (Table VI). The following parameters are used in this calculation:

(1) $T = 1 \times 10^{10}$ years.
(2) $Xe_t^{129}/Xe^{130} = 6.48$ (mean of the ratio in Murray and Earth's atmosphere). The appropriateness of this ratio is open to question, but the error introduced is likely to be small at least for meteorites with large anomalies.
(3) $K_{129}/K_{127} = 1.0$.
(4) $\tau_{129} = 23.6$ m.y.

The physical event dated by the I–Xe method is the onset of xenon retention by the meteorite-to-be. Judging from the limited evidence from heating experiments (Zähringer and Gentner, 1961; Jeffrey and Reynolds, 1961a,b), it seems likely that retention of Xe^{129} could begin only after the

---

[3] Fish and Goles (1962) have pointed out that the "primeval" xenon is probably identical with the "ambient" xenon in the internal atmosphere of the meteorite parent bodies. They proposed an ingenious method for deducing the isotopic composition of this ambient xenon by diffusion studies. Thus far the necessary measurements have been carried out on four meteorites, and the observed values for Xe^{129}/Xe^{132} show a spread of 30–40%. Evidently, the substitution of atmospheric xenon for primeval xenon in Eq. (7) is not always justified.

[4] This assumption is probably valid. For a review of the evidence, and complete references, see Jeffrey and Reynolds (1961b), Anders (1962), and Zähringer (1962).

temperature fell to some 300°K or below. The cooling time depends not only on the size of the meteorite parent body, but also on the depth of burial within the body. It is interesting that the cooling times implied by the Δt's for both the ordinary and the enstatite chondrites indicate a radius near 200 km for the meteorite parent bodies (Fig. 8). A radius of 200–300 km was previously inferred from two independent lines of evidence: the relatively small difference ($\leq 0.5 \times 10^9$ years) between the "solidification" ages (Pb–Pb, Rb–Sr) and most "gas retention" ages

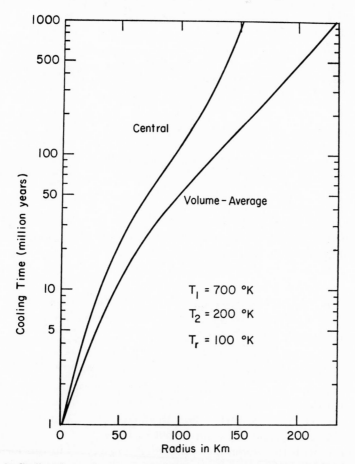

Fig. 8. Cooling times of asteroids [after Fish and Goles (1962)]. The times required for central and volume-average temperatures to fall from 700°K to 200°K were computed from the relations given by Allan and Jacobs (1956). The following assumptions were made: (1) the only heat source during cooling was K^{40}, 1.45×10^{-6} cal gm^{-1} year^{-1}; (2) thermal diffusivity $K \equiv 1 \times 10^{-2}$ cm^2 sec^{-1}; (3) the surface temperature was fixed at 100°K by radiation.

(K–Ar, U–He), and the maximum environmental temperature of chondrites consistent with Ar^{40} retention (Goles *et al.*, 1960).

The enstatite chondrites appear to be older than the other classes of meteorites. Indarch is definitely younger than the other two, implying either an earlier origin, a larger parent body, or a more deep-seated location in the parent body. For the ordinary chondrites, only two values are available, which agree rather closely. Certainly a larger statistical sample will be required before a detailed interpretation of these data can be attempted.

It is also very significant that the Sardis iron meteorite has a much larger decay interval than the chondrites just mentioned. It seems that Sardis began to retain radiogenic Xe^{129} some 130–190 m.y. later than the chondrites. This difference in relative ages is exactly the opposite of that expected from Urey's theory (1957b, 1958), according to which the chondrites consist of the debris of achondrites and irons, evolved in earlier, "primary" objects of lunar size. On the other hand, it is consistent with the view that the irons come from the cores of internally heated asteroids, which, because of their central location, would cool more slowly than the chondritic mantle (Fish *et al.*, 1960). Of course, it is possible to devise alternative, *ad hoc* histories involving larger bodies, but the complexity of these hypotheses grows with the amount of evidence to be explained. It is obviously essential to obtain further data on the relative ages of irons and stones.

For the Murray carbonaceous chondrite, a large ambiguity exists. The Xe^{129}/Xe^{136} ratio in Murray is 3.28, compared to 2.98 for the atmosphere. Taking atmospheric xenon to represent primeval xenon congenetic with Murray, one can thus compute a radiogenic Xe^{129} content of $109 \pm 11 \times 10^{-11}$ cc STP, and a decay interval of 106^{+9}_{-6} m.y. However, if the data are normalized to Xe^{130} (Kuroda, 1960), the Xe^{129}/Xe^{130} ratios are 6.48 and 6.49, corresponding to a radiogenic Xe^{129} content of $0 \pm 11 \times 10^{-11}$ cc STP, and a lower limit of ≥ 144 m.y. for the decay interval.

It can be argued (Anders, 1962) that the Xe^{130} normalization is preferable. Then the lack of radiogenic Xe^{129} in Murray, and its low K–Ar age [1.9 or ≤ 2.77 AE (Stauffer, 1961; Reynolds, 1960b)] would imply a long cooling time. However, a prolonged high-temperature era is difficult to reconcile with the presence of primordial noble gases in this meteorite (Reynolds, 1960b; Stauffer, 1961). A more satisfactory assumption would be that the radiogenic Ar^{40} and Xe^{129} are located in sites of lower retentivity than the primordial Ar^{36}, Xe^{124}, etc. Then a very mild heating would cause the loss of the former, while permitting retention of the latter. In the case of a few other meteorites at least, such differences in retentivity have indeed been demonstrated for Ar^{36} and Ar^{40} (Geiss and Hess, 1958; Zähringer and Gentner, 1961) as well as for Xe^{129} and Xe^{132} (Jeffrey and Reynolds, 1961a). Whichever explanation is finally accepted for Murray will probably apply to the other carbonaceous chondrites as well. Their xenon contents and isotopic compositions are very similar (Reynolds, 1960c; Krummenacher et al., 1962), as are their iodine contents (Goles and Anders, 1962) and K–Ar ages (Stauffer, 1961).

The I–Xe method can also provide information on the relative ages and formation conditions of individual constituents of the meteorites. Merrihue (1962) found that the chondrules in the Bruderheim chondrite were much richer in Xe^{129} than the meteorite as a whole, whereas their content of primordial xenon was much lower (Table VII). Although a

TABLE VII

XENON CONTENT OF BRUDERHEIM METEORITE

	Whole Meteorite (Clarke and Thode, 1961)	Chondrules (Merrihue, 1962)
"Normal" Xenon	$10.0 \pm 0.3 \times 10^{-10}$	2.4×10^{-10}
Excess Xe^{129}	$0.456 \pm 0.015 \times 10^{-10}$	1.3×10^{-10}
Excess Xe^{126}	$5.1 \pm 0.1 \times 10^{-13}$	$2.8 \times 10^{-13} \pm {}^{2.8}_{1.4}$

quantitative interpretation of these data cannot be made without further information on the iodine content of the chondrules, it is already apparent that these observations are in better accord with Wood's hypothesis than with any other. In Wood's model, the chondrules are early objects formed at high temperatures, where little primordial gas would be retained, while the matrix consists of fine dust condensed at lower temperatures, and is therefore probably richer in trapped gases. The differences in Xe^{129} content might reflect differences in iodine content, or in the grain size and retentivity of the iodine-bearing minerals. (See, however, Section V,B for a further discussion of these data, and a different interpretation.)

2. Plutonium-244

After the mass spectrum of meteoritic xenon became known, Kuroda (1960) pointed out that the differences between meteoritic and terrestrial xenon seemed to indicate an excess of the heavy isotopes Xe^{131}–Xe^{136} in the Earth's atmosphere. These isotopes happen to be the only ones which would be produced in substantial yield by fission of a heavy nuclide

(Khlopin and Gerling, 1948). Indeed, when the mass spectra were normalized to the shielded isotope Xe^{130} instead of the unshielded Xe^{136}, the $\Delta_i's^5$ showed a striking qualitative resemblance to a typical spontaneous fission yield curve (U^{238} or Cm^{242}), although the anomaly at mass 132 corresponded to the improbably high fission yield of $\sim 12\%$ (Kuroda, 1960).

Kuroda showed that the spontaneous fission of U^{238} during the past 4.5×10^9 years could not account for more than 2% of the observed effect, and suggested that spontaneous fission of extinct Pu^{244} (76 m.y.) and Cm^{247} (≥ 40 m.y.), or neutron-induced fission of U^{235} (0.71×10^9 years) might have produced the excess Xe^{131-6}. Indeed, the levels of Pu^{244} expected on the basis of the Wasserburg-Fowler-Hoyle model are more than sufficient to account for all the excess Xe^{131-6} now in the Earth's atmosphere.

Goles and Anders (1961) therefore argued that either the earth's atmosphere must be younger than the chondrites (Pu–Xe decay interval of the atmosphere = 290 m.y. as opposed to I–Xe intervals of 60–120 m.y. for the chondrites) or that the solar system received a smaller initial endowment of Pu^{244} than expected from the model of Wasserburg et al. (1960). The former view receives some support from the previously mentioned fact that the Earth's atmosphere has virtually the same Xe^{129}/Xe^{130} ratio as the Murray meteorite, although Murray has a thousand-fold higher xenon content per gram than the Earth. The identity in Xe^{129}/Xe^{130} ratios could, of course, be explained in terms of equal ages and fortuitously identical I/Xe ratios for the two objects, but the explanation in terms of a later origin of the Earth's atmosphere seems less contrived. Still, Cameron (1962) and Kuroda (1961) have shown that the apparent difference in age can be somewhat reduced by a different choice of parameters, and a generous allowance for possible errors in these parameters. Another possibility, to be discussed in Section V,B, is that most of the I^{129} in the early solar system was not inherited from galactic nucleosynthesis, but was produced by "last-minute synthesis" (Fowler et al., 1962) in the solar nebula. If the level of synthesis had been lower at 1 a.u. than at 2–5 a.u., then the low Xe^{129} content of the earth would merely reflect a smaller initial endowment of I^{129} and not a difference in age.

Thus far, no evidence has been obtained for fission-produced Xe^{131-6} in meteorites. The levels to be expected are quite low (10^{-11}–10^{-12} cc STP/gm) and the detection may be feasible only in meteorites with low primeval xenon content. However, a search for these minute amounts

---

[5] Defined as $(Xe^i/Xe^{130})_T/(Xe^i/Xe^{130})_M$, where the subscripts T and M stand for "terrestrial" and "meteoritic."

may well be worth the effort, since the fortuitous circumstance that two extinct radionuclides decay to isotopes of the same element, xenon, makes possible the development of a new dating method based on both I^{129} and Pu^{244} (Goles and Anders, 1961). Assuming that $t_{I\,Xe} = t_{Pu Xe}$, i.e., that the iodine- and the plutonium-bearing minerals became retentive for xenon at about the same time, one can arrange the decay equations for the two radionuclides in such a way as to eliminate or determine various unknown quantities, including the primordial I^{129}/I^{127} and Pu^{244}/U^{238} ratios, etc. Comparison of these ratios with those expected for various models of nucleosynthesis might provide some vital clues to the nature of the last nuclear events preceding the formation of the solar system. Also, once these ratios are determined, absolute ages can be calculated for all objects containing radiogenic xenon. In principle, it may thus become possible to date the origin of planets, planetary atmospheres, satellites, and meteorites to an accuracy of a few million years. Of course, this method again presupposes that the initial I^{129}/I^{127} and Pu^{244}/U^{238} ratios were uniform throughout the entire solar system.

3. Lead–205 and Palladium–107

Two other extinct radionuclides have been looked for, $\sim 24 \times 10^6$ year Pb^{205} and 6.8×10^6 year Pd^{107}. In contrast to I^{129} and Pu^{244}, their decay products (Tl^{205} and Ag^{107}) are relatively nonvolatile. Hence the fractionation between parent and daughter must have ceased at an earlier stage, presumably at the time of the last solidification of the meteoritic minerals. The temperature must have been near 1500°K at this stage, compared to ~ 300°K for the I–Xe and Pu–Xe fractionations. No enrichment of Tl^{205} was detected in 6 meteorites, and in at least one case (Canyon Diablo) the Pb/Tl fractionation was large enough to permit the calculation of a meaningful lower limit of ≥ 100 m.y. to the decay interval (Anders and and Stevens, 1960). In contrast, the silver from 3 iron meteorites, including Canyon Diablo, showed Ag^{107} enrichments of 2–4% [Table VIII

TABLE VIII

Isotopic Composition of Silver in Iron Meteorites
(From Murthy, 1960, 1962a)

Sample	Ag^{107}/Ag^{109}	Standard deviation
Toluca troilite	1.087	±0.004
Sikhote Alin	1.091	±0.005
Canyon Diablo	1.107	±0.003
Reagent AgNO$_3$	1.062–1.066	±0.002

(Murthy, 1960, 1962a)]. Allowing for some uncertainty in the Pd/Ag ratio, and the Ag^{107} content of primeval silver, these enrichments correspond to decay intervals around $(0 \pm 20) \times 10^6$ years.

To account for the difference between this result and the I–Xe decay interval of the Sardis iron in Table IV, it is merely necessary to assume that the cooling time of the cores of the meteorite parent bodies from ~1500°K, where Pd/Ag fractionations ceased, to ~300°K, where Xe^{129} retention began, was the order of 2×10^8 years. Such times are consistent with other estimates.

On the other hand, the difference between the Pd^{107}–Ag^{107} and Pb^{205}–Tl^{205} decay intervals calls for further special assumptions, such as an error in the estimate of the abundance of Pb^{205} at t_0. Another possibility is the preferential production of Pd^{107} at a relatively late stage in the formation of the solar system (Anders, 1961; Fowler et al., 1962; Murthy and Urey, 1962). It is difficult, however, to conceive of an event that would produce Pd^{107} at levels of several percent the abundance of neighboring nuclides, without, at the same time, also raising the abundances of longer-lived extinct nuclides. Finally, one must consider the possibility that the measurements themselves may be in error. Data by Chakraburtty et al. (1962), though in part of lower accuracy, show no perceptible Ag^{107} enrichment in a number of iron meteorites, including two of those studied by Murthy (Canyon Diablo and Toluca), and the nickel-rich ataxite Piñon whose high Pd/Ag ratio (400–900) would lead one to expect an Ag^{107} anomaly of $\geq 20\%$ if it were congenetic with Canyon Diablo. For Canyon Diablo itself, six separate determinations gave Ag^{107} anomalies of 0 ± 13, 0 ± 13, -5 ± 9, -12 ± 13, 3 ± 3, and $6 \pm 3\%_0$. The weighted mean of these 6 analyses is $2 \pm 2\%_0$, compared to Murthy's value of $40 \pm 4\%_0$. The reason for the discrepancies between the two sets of data is not known, but it would seem that no firm conclusions can be drawn in regard to the presence of extinct Pd^{107} in meteorites.

B. General Isotopic Anomalies

Another clue of great potential significance is provided by the "general" isotopic anomalies in meteorites. Reynolds (1960a) noted that in addition to the anomaly at mass number 129, meteoritic and terrestrial xenon differed at other mass numbers as well (Fig. 9).

Differences at heavier mass numbers can probably be explained in terms of a fission contribution to terrestrial xenon, as noted above. For the lighter mass numbers, three different interpretations have been proposed.

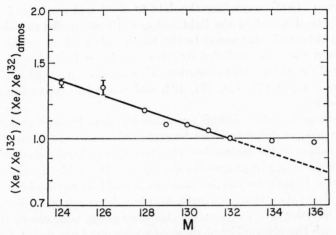

FIG. 9. Isotopic composition of Murray xenon relative to atmospheric xenon [after Reynolds (1960b)]. Lighter isotopes are present in excess.

Goles and Anders (1961) normalize the data to Xe^{130}; they find an excess of the lighter isotopes in meteoritic xenon and attribute this to charged-particle induced spallation reactions in the solar nebula. Such reactions would be expected to product the light, neutron-deficient isotopes in relatively high yields, and since these isotopes are normally rare, even a small incremental amount can cause a disproportionately large change in their relative abundance. The isotopic differences between meteoritic and terrestrial xenon are then attributed to the lower density of matter in the asteroidal belt, which may lead to higher levels of particle acceleration and spallation.

A detailed model for charged-particle acceleration in the solar nebula was proposed by Fowler et al. (1962), in an attempt to explain the abundance of D, Li, Be, and B, and their isotopic composition. They suggest that intense irradiation with 500 Mev protons and thermal neutrons took place at a time when most planetary and meteoritic matter was contained in meter-sized planetesimals. The dimensions of the planetesimals must have been such that on the average only some 10% of the material was strongly irradiated.[6]

---

[6] It now appears doubtful whether thermal neutron reactions occurred at anything like the levels postulated by Fowler et al. Murthy and Schmitt (1962) have shown that the nuclides Sm^{149} and Gd^{157}, with thermal neutron capture cross sections of 40,800,900, and 250,000 barns, occur in exactly the same isotopic abundance in meteoritic and terrestrial matter. To explain this in terms of the above model, it is necessary to assume that the mixing ratios of irradiated and unirradiated material were exactly identical at 1 a.u. and at 2–5 a.u.

Cameron (1962) normalizes the data to Xe^{128}, and considers terrestrial xenon to be deficient in the light isotopes. He attributes this deficiency to the addition of solar xenon to the Earth's atmosphere, assuming that solar xenon was once irradiated by 100 ev neutrons during the deuterium-burning stage of the sun's evolution. This irradiation would slightly deplete the isotopes 124, 126, 131, 134, and 136, while enhancing isotopes 128 and 130.

Krummenacher et al. (1962) normalize the data to Xe^{136} and conclude that the isotopic differences can be explained by: (a) addition of fission-product xenon to the meteorites; (b) strong mass-fractionation of terrestrial xenon, leading to progressive depletion of the lighter isotopes.

All three hypotheses can be made to account in some ad hoc manner for the observation that meteoritic krypton shows much smaller anomalies, of the order of 2% or less. On this basis alone, none can be disqualified, though the plausibility of these ad hoc assumptions varies. However, two additional pieces of evidence have recently become available that have a bearing on this question.

Umemoto (1962) has observed an enrichment of the lighter isotopes in meteoritic barium that is qualitatively very similar to that in xenon (Fig. 10). Barium is a nonvolatile element and hence neither the mechanism of Cameron nor that of Krummenacher et al., can be invoked to

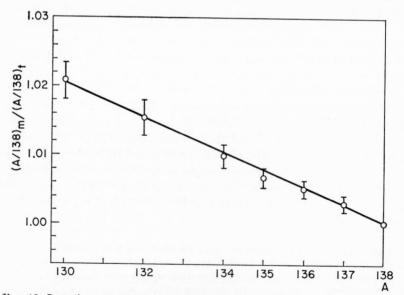

Fig. 10. Isotopic composition of meteoritic barium relative to terrestrial barium (Umemoto, 1962). The three meteorites are the ordinary chondrite Bruderheim and the calcium-rich achondrites Nuevo Laredo and Pasamonte.

explain the anomalies without further *ad hoc* assumptions, since both depend on the fractionation or transport of gases.

Moreover, Merrihue (1962) has found that the chondrules in Bruderheim show a strong enrichment of Xe^{124} and Xe^{126}, relative to "normal" xenon (Table VII). When the chondrules are heated to progressively higher temperatures, the Xe^{124}/Xe^{132} and Xe^{126}/Xe^{132} ratios rise, until maximum anomalies of 2400 and 3800‰ are reached at 1100°C (Fig. 11). Previously, analyses of meteorite xenon had always given virtually constant anomalies at mass numbers 124 and 126, clustering around the average values for carbonaceous chondrite xenon: 361 ± 52 and 309 ± 63‰. Apparently not only Xe^{129}, but also $Xe^{124,126}$ are present in the meteorite as separate components, wholly distinct from the primordial component represented by Xe^{132} and the other heavy xenon isotopes (Fig. 12). In contrast to Xe^{129}, the lighter xenon isotopes do not have a long-lived radioactive progenitor, and it seems necessary to conclude that the excess $Xe^{124,126}$ was generated *in situ* by some nuclear process, most probably spallation by charged particles.

Recent production by cosmic rays is a marginal possibility. As already pointed out by Reynolds (1960b) for several other meteorites, the anomalous $Xe^{124,126}$ shows no correlation with the cosmic-ray exposure age. In the present instance, it is barely possible that the level of cosmic-ray irradiation inferred from the lighter spallation products [He^3, Ne^{21}, and Ar^{38} (see Table IX)] might account for the $Xe^{124,126}$, if the chondrules contained an amount of barium that was larger than usual (Merrihue, 1962), and if the production cross section of Xe^{126} were as high as 10^{-2} barns.

Alternately, an earlier era of irradiation might be postulated. Some arbitrary assumption will be required to account for the absence of the lighter spallation products from that era.

It is possible to deduce a few boundary conditions for this process. Owing to the short range of charged particles, the irradiation must have occurred while the meteoritic matter was dispersed in space as aggregates of no more than meter dimensions, and possibly after some of the nebular gas had been dissipated. To permit retention of xenon, the chondrules must not have been heated strongly after the irradiation, except, perhaps, in a closed system. This implies either that the irradiation occured *after* the high-luminosity stage of the sun, or that the chondrules had already accreted to larger, well-insulated bodies at the onset of the high-luminosity stage. Yet it is necessary to assume *some* heating, sufficient to expel the lighter noble gases, but not sufficient to homogenize the Xe^{132} and $Xe^{124,126}$. In principle, this could have happened during metamorphism in the meteorite parent body (Wood, 1962b).

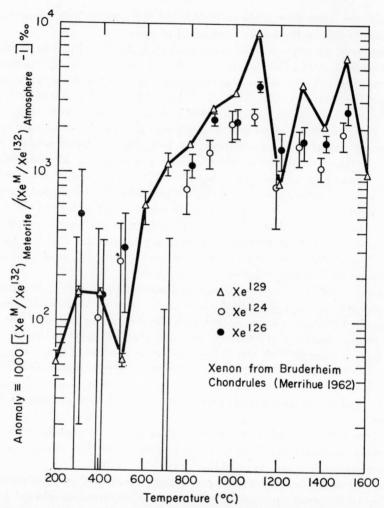

FIG. 11. Excess Xe^{124,126,129} in chondrules from Bruderheim meteorite, evolved during 1 hour at each temperature. The change of the Xe^{124}/Xe^{132} and Xe^{126}/Xe^{132} ratios with temperature, and the high values in the range 800°–1500°C indicate that Xe^{124,126} are present in the meteorite as separate components, distinct from the (primordial) Xe^{132} component. Possibly the light isotopes were made by charged-particle reactions. Compare the Xe^{124,126} anomalies with those in Fig. 9, which were previously regarded as typical of *all* meteoritic xenon.

Perhaps the most troublesome requirement is that the metal particles in chondrites must have differentiated into kamacite and taenite at some time between the initial high-temperature stage and the final cooling of the meteorite parent bodies. This differentiation requires slow cooling

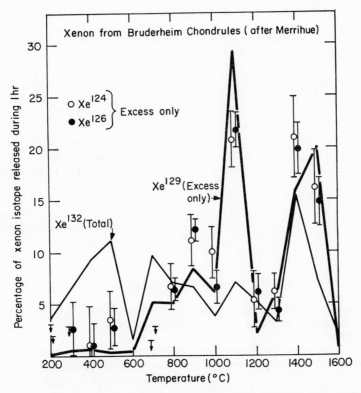

Fig. 12. Xenon in chondrules from Bruderheim meteorite (Merrihue, 1962). The isotopes $Xe^{124,126,129}$ are evolved in nearly identical patterns, which suggests an identical distribution within the chondrules, and hence perhaps an identical origin. The isotope Xe^{132}, which is largely of primordial origin, seems to go its own ways.

through the temperature range 600°–400°C. There is good evidence that this differentiation can proceed *in situ* (Anders, 1960) and it may therefore have occurred in the immediate parent bodies of the chondrites, rather than in an earlier generation of "primary" objects (Urey, 1956, 1959; Urey and Mayeda, 1959). However, it is difficult to imagine how two separate xenon components could persist at the temperatures in question without complete redistribution and homogenization. Regardless which model is used, the conclusion seems inescapable that at least one of the two xenon components was introduced at a late stage, after the final cooling of meteoritic matter. This makes the cosmic-ray origin of the $Xe^{124,126}$ look very appealing. If an early origin of the Xe is assumed instead, then there is no obvious way of deciding which component came last. But since it was shown in Section III that the primordial gases were

TABLE IX

Age Determinations on Bruderheim Chondrite

Method	Age 10⁹ years	Ref.[a]	Interpretation
I^{129}–Xe^{129}	0.123^b	a, b	Cooling to $<300°K$
K^{40}–Ar^{40}	1.6	c	Storage at $300°K > T > 200°K$ followed by abrupt temperature drop. (Breakup to $100 \text{ km} > r > 10 \text{ m}$?)
(U, Th)–He^4	1.5	c	
H^3–He^3	0.024	c	Breakup to meter-sized fragments resulting in strong irradiation by cosmic rays
H^3–He^3	0.035	d	
Ar^{39}–Ar^{38}	0.026	d	
Cl^{36}–Ar^{36}	0.033	e	
Na^{22}–Ne^{22}	0.027	e	

[a] References:
  a. Clarke and Thode (1961)   d. Fireman and DeFelice (1961)
  b. Goles and Anders (1961)   e. Honda *et al.* (1961)
  c. Signer (1961)

[b] The I–Xe decay interval is reckoned *forward* in time, from the cessation of nucleosynthesis, whereas all other ages are measured *backward* in time, starting from the present.

definitely introduced at a late stage in at least a few meteorites, and possibly in all others, one can tentatively assume that the $Xe^{124,126}$ was produced in chondrules or some other part of meteoritic matter at an early stage, and remained associated with it during residence in the parent body, where as the primordial Xe^{132}, etc., being concentrated preferentially in another fraction of the primitive condensate, was not incorporated in the meteoritic matter until after the end of the last high-temperature stage. Of course, some reason must be found why the fraction carrying the primordial gases was not also rich in $Xe^{124,126}$. One possibility is that the spallation-produced $Xe^{124,126}$ were lost by recoil from the micron-sized dust carrying adsorbed primordial gases. In the absence of any further clues, room for speculation on this question is almost unlimited.

Of course, if the excess $Xe^{124,126}$ was produced by charged-particle reactions, then some I^{129} should have been made also. The excess Xe^{126} is a factor of ~500 less abundant than the excess Xe^{129} (8×10^{-13} gm Xe^{129}/gm), but even the latter amount is minute compared to the cumulative abundance of the elements immediately above xenon (Cs–Nd, ~6 ppm), and could be accounted for by a moderate level of spallation (integrated flux of $10^{19} - 10^{20}$ protons cm^{-2}). The lower relative abundance of $Xe^{124,126}$ can be attributed to a partial diffusion loss at a time when most of the Xe^{129} was still in the form of the relatively nonvolatile I^{129}. It is interesting that the model of Fowler *et al.* (1962) predicts a spallation yield of 8 × 10^{-11} gm I^{129}/gm for the strongly irradiated portion of planetary matter. This is a factor of 100 higher than the observed Xe^{129} content of the Bruderheim chondrules.

An interesting consequence of such a spallation era is that a substantial amount of 0.74 × 10^6 year Al^{26} should be produced also. This nuclide would provide a suitable heat source for melting and differentiation in some of the meteorite parent bodies (Urey, 1955; Fish *et al.*, 1960).

If the I^{129} was indeed produced by charged-particle reactions during some late stage in the evolution of the solar nebula, then there is no assurance that the level of spallation, and hence the yield of I^{129}, was constant throughout the nebula. Particle acceleration would be more efficient at the low densities prevailing in the asteroidal belt than at the high densities prevailing in the asteroidal belt than at the high densities near the Earth's orbit. Then the surprisingly small amount of radiogenic Xe^{129} in terrestrial xenon (Anders and Goles, 1961; Butler *et al.*, 1962) does not necessarily imply a younger age of the Earth, but, more likely, a smaller production of I^{129} in the region from which the Earth accreted. As already mentioned, such regional variations in the I^{129}/I^{127} ratio would seriously limit the applicability of the dating methods discussed in Section V,A.

Were it only for the Ba, Kr, and Xe data, the present evidence would seem to suggest some type of nuclear process that affected meteoritic matter to a greater extent than terrestrial matter. Such a process should have produced isotopic anomalies in many other elements as well. Earlier workers failed to detect isotopic differences in many elements isolated from meteorites (Brown, 1949b; Schmitt *et al.*, 1960; Reed *et al.*, 1960), but since the differences appear to be the order of 2% or less for a nonvolatile element, such as Ba, it is possible that many anomalies were missed due to insufficient sensitivity of the analytical methods employed.

Some of the most recent data are, however, inconsistent with the spallation mechanism, or, for that matter, any of the previously discussed mechanisms. Umemoto (1962) did not detect any anomalies in meteoritic cerium (an element only two atomic numbers above barium) although its lightest isotopes are only about twice as abundant as those of barium. Even more puzzling are the data on molybdenum (Murthy, 1962b). Some iron meteorites appeared to contain normal molybdenum, whereas others showed mass-dependent anomalies of up to 7%. In contrast to Ba and Xe, the light isotopes were *depleted* relative to their terrestrial abundances. It seems that the only way to account for all the data is to assume that the solar nebula was isotopically inhomogeneous, owing to incomplete mixing in its parent dust cloud. Even so, the persistence of gross isotopic inhomogeneities in as highly differentiated materials as iron meteorites calls for some further *ad hoc* assumptions.

Clearly, the general isotopic anomalies are of great potential value in delineating the nuclear history of the solar system, since isotopic data are less ambiguous than chemical data, in principle, and can thus lead to firmer conclusions. At the present time, the data do not fit into a neat pattern, and it may be best to await a confirmation of some of these measurements before attempting a detailed interpretation.

VI. Conclusions

Urey (1962a) has recently outlined a series of possible events in the history of the solar system that would account for the evidence, while remaining in accord with physical possibilities. The events suggested are:

"(1) Early in its history the sun acquired a nebula whose plane was that of the ecliptic. This nebula may have resulted from a separation of the disc from the sun during the latter's evolution from a dust cloud, and this separation may have been aided by magnetic fields. Or, the sun may have captured the nebula by collision with a small dust cloud early in its history. I regard this latter suggestion as improbable.

"(2) Within this solar nebula lunar-sized objects of the composition of the non-volatile fraction of cosmic matter were formed. The objects became heated to high temperatures, possibly by chemical heating or heating in a convection polytrope, and developed the characteristic kamacite and taenite iron-nickel phases of the chondritic meteorites.

"(3) At least in that region from which the meteorites originated, these objects were broken into small fragments by some marked crushing action. These processes occurred 4.5 AE ago.

"(4) There is some evidence that the lunar objects formed throughout the region of the terrestrial planets, and that they broke up into small fragments. The silicate fraction was selectively lost from the region of the terrestrial planets, resulting in an increased iron content of all these planets and a variable mean density due to the different degrees of silicate loss.

"(5) The gases were lost in the region of the terrestrial planets while the solid materials were at low temperatures.

"(6) The solid objects collected into the terrestrial planets probably so slowly that their general temperatures were low. It is likely that these planets have never been completely melted.

"(7) Uranus and Neptune have also lost their volatiles, but these included only such substances as are gaseous at low temperatures. This circumstance indicates that temperatures during the loss of gases were similar to those in the solar system at the present time.

"(8) Jupiter and Saturn retained their volatiles. This indicates that their accumulation process proceeded more rapidly so that high gravitational fields, capable of holding gases, developed. The absence of a planet in the asteroidal belt may be due to the reverse process, i.e., dissipation proceeded more rapidly than accumulation, and most of the material in this region was lost.

"(9) The moon may be one of the primary lunar-sized objects. Its size, mass and composition as indicated by its density are in accord with this view. It may also be that the other lunar-sized satellites of the solar system are primary objects which have escaped break-up and capture during the accumulation of the planets.

"(10) It is likely that radioactive heating, heating by an initially high-temperature sun, synthesis of some elements by high-energy protons and other processes, played some or essential roles in the history as well."

Except for points (2), (3), and (4), this outline is very much in accord with the views of the writer, and the evidence presented in this chapter. An alternative outline, covering the first five points, follows.

(1) The material comprising the solar nebula cooled rapidly from high initial temperatures, leading to the formation of chondrules, metal grains, and other solid particles.

(2) The nebula was irradiated by charged particles, the level of irradiation varying with distance from the sun. The material from which the chondrites formed was not outgassed strongly after this stage; hence the sun must have gone through its high-luminosity era before stage (2) or toward the end of stage (3).

(3) The planets and meteorite parent bodies accreted at low temperatures. Some time during stages (1)–(3) a fractionation of metal and silicate particles took place, based on differences in density, magnetic susceptibility, or brittleness. Some time during stages (1)–(3), before the terrestrial planets had grown to a large enough size to hold gases gravitationally, the gases were lost.

(4) The meteorite parent bodies were heated to a varying degree by a transient heat source of unknown nature (possibly an extinct radioactivity, such as Al^{26}); some to melting temperatures (permitting the formation of achondrites and irons) and others to temperatures near 500°C where metamorphism could take place and the metal particles in chondrites could differentiate to kamacite and taenite. After final cooling, some redistribution of noble gases took place, possibly by shock.

The differences between these two outlines are entirely due to subjective differences in judgment. The issues on which Urey's and the writer's views differ most widely are: whether there was an early high-temperature stage; whether lunar-sized objects played a special role in the development of the meteorites and planets; whether the metal particles in chondrites could have acquired their structures *in situ*; and whether iron meteorites formed as individual entities or as fragments of larger objects. As these issues are resolved by further experimental and theoretical work, the two outlines are likely to approach each other more and more closely.

ACKNOWLEDGMENT

This work was supported in part by the U. S. Atomic Energy Commission.

REFERENCES

Allan, D. W., and Jacobs, J. A. (1956) *Geochim. et Cosmochim. Acta* **9**, 256.

Anders, E. (1960) Unpublished work.

Anders, E. (1961) *Z. Naturforsch.* **16a**, 520.

Anders, E. (1962) *Revs. Modern Phys.* **34**, (in press). (A more up-to-date version of this paper is to appear in "The Solar System" (G. P. Kuiper and B. M. Middlehurst, eds.), Vol. IV. Univ. of Chicago Press, Chicago.)

Anders, E. (1963) *Ann. N. Y. Acad. Sci.* (in press).

Anders, E., and Goles, G. G. (1961) *J. Chem. Ed.* **38**, 58.

Anders, E., and Stevens, C. M. (1960) *J. Geophys. Research* **65**, 3043.

Brown, H. (1947) *Phys. Rev.* **72**, 348.

Brown, H. (1949a) *In* "The Atmospheres of the Earth and Planets" (G. P. Kuiper, ed.) Univ. of Chicago Press, Chicago, Illinois.

Brown, H. (1949b). *Revs. Modern Phys.* **21**, 625.

Burbidge, E. M., Burbidge, G. R., Fowler, W. A., and Hoyle, F. (1957) *Revs. Modern Phys.* **29**, 548.

Butler, M. M., Jeffrey, P., Reynolds, J. H., and Wasserburg, G. J. (1962) Conf. on Nuclear Geophysics, Woods Hole, Massachusetts, June 7–9.

Cameron, A. G. W. (1959a) *Astrophys. J.* **129**, 676.

Cameron, A. G. W. (1959b). Personal communication.

Cameron, A. G. W. (1962) *Icarus* **1**, 13–69.

Chakraburtty, A. K., Rushing, H. C., Stevens, C. M., and Anders, E. To be published.

Clarke, W. B., and Thode, H. G. (1961) *J. Geophys. Research* **66**, 3578.

DuFresne, E. R., and Anders, E. (1962a) *Geochim. et Cosmochim. Acta* (in press).

DuFresne, E. R., and Anders, E. (1962b) *Geochim. et Cosmochim. Acta* **26**, 251.

Eberhardt, P., and Eberhardt, A. (1961) *Z. Naturforsch.* **16a**, 236.

Edwards, G., and Urey, H. C. (1955) *Geochim. et Cosmochim. Acta* **7**, 154.

Ehmann, W. D., and Huizenga, J. R. (1959) *Geochim. et Cosmochim. Acta* **17**, 125.

Fireman, E. L., and DeFelice, J. (1961) *J. Geophys. Research* **66**, 3547.

Fish, R. A., and Goles, G. G. (1962) To be published.

Fish, R. A., Goles, G. G., and Anders, E. (1960) *Astrophys. J.* **132**, 243.

Fowler, W. A., Greenstein, J. P., and Hoyle, F. (1962) *Geophys. J.* **6**, 148–220.

Frederiksson, K. (1962) Personal communication.

Fredriksson, K., and Keil, K. (1963) To be published.

Geiss, J. (1957) *Chimia (Switz.)* **11**, 349.

Geiss, J., and Hess, D. C. (1958) *Astrophys. J.* **124**, 224.

Gerling, E. K., and Levskii, L. K. (1956) *Doklady Akad. Nauk S.S.S.R.* **110**, 750.

Gold, T. (1961) *J. Geophys. Research* **66**, 2531.

Goldschmidt, V. M. (1937) Geochemische Verteilungsgesetze der Elemente IX. *Skrifter Norske Videnskaps.-Akad. Oslo, I, Math.-Naturv. Kl.* **1937**, No. 4.

Goles, G. G., and Anders, E. (1960) *J. Geophys. Research* **65**, 4181.

Goles, G. G., and Anders, E. (1961) *J. Geophys. Research* **66**, 889.

Goles, G. G., and Anders, E. (1962) *Geochim. et Cosmochim. Acta* **26**, 723.

Goles, G. G., Fish, R. A., and Anders, E. (1960) *Geochim. et Cosmochim. Acta* **19**, 177.

Herbig, G. (1961) *Proc. Lunar & Planetary Colloq.* **2** (4), 64.

Honda, M., Umemoto, S., and Arnold, J. R. (1961) *J. Geophys. Research* **66**, 3541.

Jeffrey, P. M., and Reynolds, J. H. (1961a). *Z. Naturforsch.* **16a**, 431.

Jeffrey, P. M., and Reynolds, J. H. (1961b) *J. Geophys. Research* **66**, 3582.

Khlopin, V. G., and Gerling, E. K. (1948) *Doklady Akad. Nauk S.S.S.R.* **61**, 297.

Könog, H., Keil, K., Hintenberger, H., Wlotzka, F., and Begemann, F. (1961) *Z. Naturforsch.* **16a**, 1124.

Kohman, T. P. (1956) *Proc. N. Y. Acad. Sci.* **62**, 503.

Kohman, T. P. (1961) *J. Chem. Ed.* **38**, 73.

Krummenacher, D., Merrihue, C. M., Pepin, R. O., and Reynolds, J. H. (1962) *Geochim. et Cosmochim. Acta* **26**, 231.

Kuroda, P. K. (1960) *Nature* **187**, 36.

Kuroda, P. K. (1961) *Geochim. et Cosmochim. Acta* **24**, 40.

Latimer, W. M. (1950) *Science* **112**, 101.

Lazarus, D. (1960) *Proc. Conf. on the Use of Radioisotopes in the Physical Sciences and Industry* RICC/188.

Levin, B. J. (1958) *Chem. Erde* **19**, 286–295.

Liller, W. (1960) *Astrophys. J.* **132**, 867.

Lovering, J. F. (1957) *Geochim. et Cosmochim. Acta* **12**, 253.

Mason, B. (1960) *J. Geophys. Research* **65**, 2965.

Merrinue, C. M. (1962) *J. Geophys. Research* **67**, in press.

Miller, S. L. (1961) *Proc. Natl. Acad. Sci. U. S.* **47**, 1798.

Murthy, V. R. (1960) *Phys. Rev. Letters* **5**, 539.

Murthy, V. R. (1962a) *Geochim. et Cosmochim. Acta* **26**, 481.

Murthy, V. R. (1962b) *J. Geophys. Research* **67**, 905.

Murthy, V. R., and Schmitt, R. A. (1962) Submitted to *J. Geophys. Research*.

Murthy, V. R., and Urey, H. C. (1962) *Astrophys. J.* **135**, 626.

Nagy, B., Meinschein, W. G., and Hennessy, D. J. (1962) To be published.

Parkin, D. W., Hunter, W., and Brownlow, A. E. (1962) *Nature* **193**, 639–42.

Reed, G. W., Kigoshi, K., and Turkevich, A. (1960) *Geochim. et Cosmochim. Acta* **20**, 122.

Reynolds, J. H. (1960a) *Phys. Rev. Letters* **4**, 8.

Reynolds, J. H. (1960b) *Phys. Rev. Letters* **4**, 351.

Reynolds, J. H. (1960c) *J. Geophys. Research* **65**, 3843.

Reynolds, J. H., and Lipson, J. I. (1957) *Geochim. et Cosmochim. Acta* **12**, 330.

Reynolds, J. H., Merrihue, C. M., and Pepin, R. O. (1962) *Bull. Am. Phys. Soc.* [2] **7**, 35.

Ringwood, A. E. (1959) *Geochim. et Cosmochim. Acta* **15**, 257.

Ringwood, A. E. (1961) *Geochim. et Cosmochim. Acta* **24**, 159.

Russell, H. N., and Menzel, D. H. (1933) *Proc. Natl. Acad. Sci. U. S.* **19**, 997.

Schindewolf, U., and Wahlgren, M. (1960) *Geochim. et Cosmochim. Acta* **18**, 36.

Schmitt, R. A. (1962) *Geochim. et Cosmochim. Acta* (in press).

Schmitt, R. A., Mosen, A. W., Suffredini, C. S., Lasch, J. E., Sharp, R. A., and Olehy, D. A. (1960) *Nature* **186**, 863.

Signer, P. (1961) *J. Geophys. Research* **66**, 2560.

Signer, P., and Suess, H. E. (1962) To be published.

Stauffer, H. (1961) *Geochim. et Cosmochim. Acta* **24**, 70.

Suess, H. E. (1947) *Z. Naturforsch.* **2a**, 604.

Suess, H. E. (1948) *Z. Elektrochem.* **53**, 237.

Suess, H. E. (1949) *J. Geol.* **57**, 600.

Suess, H. E. (1962) Personal communication.

Suess, H. E., and Urey, H. C. (1956) *Revs. Modern Phys.* **28**, 53.

Umemoto, S. (1962) *J. Geophys. Research* **67**, 375.

Urey, H. C. (1952a) "The Planets." Yale Univ. Press, New Haven, Connecticut.

Urey, H. C. (1952b) *In* "L. Farkas Memorial Volume." Research Council of Israel Spec. Publ. No. 1, Jerusalem, Israel.

Urey, H. C. (1954) *Astrophys. J. Suppl.* No. 1, 147.

Urey, H. C. (1955) *Proc. Natl. Acad. Sci. U. S.* **41**, 127.

Urey, H. C. (1956) *Astrophys. J.* **124**, 623.

Urey, H. C. (1957a) *Progr. Phys. and Chem. Earth* **2**, 46.

Urey, H. C. (1957b) 41st Guthrie Lecture. *Yearbook Phys. Soc. (London)* p. 14.

Urey, H. C. (1958) *Proc. Chem. Soc.* p. 67.

Urey, H. C. (1959) *J. Geophys. Research* **64**, 1721.

Urey, H. C. (1960) *Geochim. et Cosmochim. Acta* **18**, 151.

Urey, H. C. (1961) *J. Geophys. Research* **66**, 1988.

Urey, H. C. (1962a) *Geochim. et Cosmochim. Acta* **26**, 1–13.

Urey, H. C. (1962b) *Nature* **193**, 1119.

Urey, H. C., and Craig, H. (1953) *Geochim. et Cosmochim. Acta* **4**, 36.

Urey, H. C., and Donn, B. (1956) *Astrophys. J.* **124**, 307.

Urey, H. C., and Mayeda, T. (1959) *Geochim. et Cosmochim. Acta* **17**, 113.

Vogel, R. (1961) *Chem. Erde* **21**, 24.

Wasserburg, G. J., and Hayden, R. J. (1955) *Nature* **176**, 130.

Wasserburg, G. J., Fowler, W. A., and Hoyle, F. (1960) *Phys. Rev. Letters* **4**, 112.

Watson, K., Murray, B. C., and Brown, H. (1961) *J. Geophys. Research* **66**, 3033.

Wiik, H. B. (1956) *Geochim. et Cosmochim. Acta* **9**, 279.

Wood, J. A. (1958) Silicate meteorite structures and the origin of meteorites. Smithsonian Astrophys. Obs. Tech. Rept. No. 10, Cambridge, Massachusetts.

Wood, J. A. (1962a) *Nature* **194**, 127.

Wood, J. A. (1962b) *Geochim. et Cosmochim. Acta* **26**, 739.

Zähringer, J. (1962) *Z. Naturforsch.* **17a** (in press).

Zähringer, J., and Gentner, W. (1961) *Z. Naturforsch.* **16a**, 239.

Properties of Chondrules—I

H. E. SUESS

University of California, San Diego, La Jolla, California

The interpretation of data from meteorites depends very much on what one assumes to be the mechanism of their formation. My old pet idea, that I obtained some thirty or forty years ago, mainly from people of the previous generation, was that meteoritic chondrules are products that have directly condensed from a gas phase. About ten years ago I discussed this possibility with Dr. Urey, who rejected it on three different independent grounds. Until recently it did not seem possible to contradict Dr. Urey's objections, but there are now, in my opinion, reasons for resuming the argument.

The first difficulty pointed out by Dr. Urey was the fact that oxidized iron is present in chondrules. Latimer and others concluded, from the constant of the equilibrium

$$FeO + H_2 = Fe + H_2O$$

that, with a primeval ratio of H_2 to H_2O of about 1000, the iron will be reduced and in the form of metal at all temperatures above 600°K. Therefore, molten droplets that solidified into chondrules containing oxidized iron cannot have condensed from a gas of primeval composition.

The second argument against the formation of chondrules from a gas phase is based on the fact that there seemed to be different types of chondrules, some consisting of metal only, others consisting of sulfide, others of olivine, feldspar, and so on. Dr. Urey pointed out that it is impossible to get such types of chondrules simultaneously from the gas phase.

The third objection comes from the fact that in order to obtain chondrules from a gas phase, pressure and temperature have to be above the triple point of the condensing material. The astronomical theories of the origin of the solar system do not, in general, include a stage at which such conditions prevail.

Perhaps we can argue about these three points in the following way:

The first objection concerns the occurrence of oxidized iron. Of course, no oxidized iron will form as long as the ratio of hydrogen to water is equal to the primeval ratio of 1000, but Fowler and Hoyle have postulated in their chapters that hydrogen leaves and condensable material is retained at a very early stage of the formation of the solar system. With Dr. Fowler's ratio of hydrogen to condensable material, all the iron will be oxidized and no metallic iron will be present. Some types of chondrites represent such an extreme case, whereas others—the enstatite chondrites—represent the other extreme and do not contain any oxidized iron. The majority of meteorites are composed of material that looks as if it formed under conditions lying between these two extremes.

In addition to the theoretical arguments advanced by Fowler and Hoyle, there are empirical data that indicate that hydrogen and the light gases were separated from the heavier gases and from condensable material at an early stage of the solar system. Figure 3 of the chapter by Anders, shows the fractions of the rare gases present in the earth's atmosphere and in certain types of gas-containing meteorites compared to the composition of primeval solar matter. The logarithm of the fraction of rare gas retained is plotted against its atomic weight. You see that for the earth, about 10^{-7} parts of xenon originally present were retained.

The fraction of neon retained is approximately four orders of magnitude smaller. A very effective mechanism that separated xenon from neon must have prevailed. Some time ago I discussed possibilities for this mechanism and pointed out that separation in the gas phase, through differences in the rate of escape from a gravitational field due to the mass differences, seemed to be the most plausible one. Such mechanism of separation will also lead to a depletion of hydrogen and to increasingly oxidizing conditions under which chondrules containing oxidized iron could have formed.

The second argument concerns the mineralogical composition of the chondrules. This at present is a subject of intensive studies at various laboratories. At La Jolla, Dr. Kurt Fredericksson, using an electron microprobe in Dr. Gustaf Arrhenius's laboratory, found that individual chondrules do, in general, contain various minerals such as metallic iron and sulfides, as well as ortho- and meta-silicates. Monomineralic chondrules are unusual exceptions. Therefore, it does not appear impossible that the minerals in chondrules have crystallized from the molten droplets that condensed out of a gas, as far as mineralogical evidence is concerned.

The third argument, concerning the high pressures and temperatures necessary to get liquid droplets from the gas phase, must be discussed from the point of view of theories of the formation of the solar system. I wonder if it is not possible to modify existing theories in such a way that the necessary conditions could have prevailed at certain times. These necessary conditions can be calculated from theoretical data. Dr. Urey carried out the calculations a long time ago with thermodynamic data that he had estimated himself. More recently, revised data have been published by a joint panel of the Army, Navy, and Air Force. The new data are not significantly different from Dr. Urey's earlier estimates. Magnesium silicate, for example, is volatilized under reducing conditions according to the equation:

$$MgSiO_3 + 2H_2 = Mg + SiO + 2H_2O$$

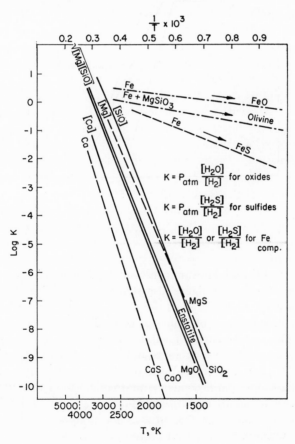

FIG. 1.

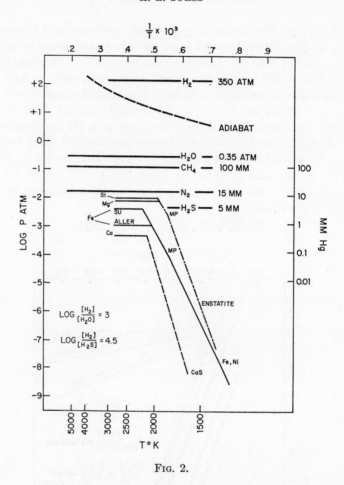

FIG. 2.

Figure 1 shows the equilibrium constant of this reaction for $H_2O/H_2 = 1$ as a function of $1/T$. The figure also shows the constants for other equilibria as indicated. Figure 2 gives the vapor pressure of iron, magnesium, and calcium in a medium of primeval composition and a total hydrogen pressure of 350 atm. In such a medium the partial water pressure will be 0.35 atm; CH_4 will have a pressure of about 100 mm Hg; nitrogen, 50 mm; and H_2S, about 5 mm. With decreasing temperatures, at about 2000°K liquid droplets will condense to a composition resembling that of the chondrules found in enstatite chondrites. A primeval mixture containing about two orders of magnitude, less hydrogen, and leaving other constituents unchanged, will lead to the presence of oxidized iron in the silicates.

Properties of Chondrules—II

J. A. WOOD

Enrico Fermi Institute for Nuclear Studies, University of Chicago, Chicago, Illinois, and Smithsonian Astrophysical Observatory, Cambridge, Massachusetts

The terrestrial planets are thought by most writers to have accreted from small solid particles or planetesimals. The possibility exists that chondrules, the small (usually <3 mm in diameter) spheres and spheroids of silicate and metallic minerals which are characteristic of chondritic meteorites, are surviving planetesimals. As such, they deserve careful study.

Typical chondrules from the chondrite Bjurbole are shown in Fig. 1. The diverse mineralogies and textures in chondrules may be studied by making thin-sections (slices mounted on glass slides and ground down to ∼0.03 mm thickness) of them, which can be viewed microscopically by transmitted light. Figure 2 shows thin-sections of two of the most commonly occurring chondrule types.

Hardly any of the chondrules appear to be truly monomineralic. Many obviously contain several minerals, and most of the rest consist of one predominant mineral plus a glassy or cryptocrystalline material. The boundary condition that Urey (1952) has imposed on the chondrule-forming process—that it must produce monomineralic chondrules—does not seem to be required.

Most writers have concluded that chondrules were once dispersed molten droplets. Suggestive of this is their spherical form; the volcanic mineralogy and texture of many chondrules (for example, that in Fig. 2a); the presence of glass in some chondrules; and the indentation of some chondrules by others, indicating plastic behavior (Fig. 3).

Almost all the chondrites in our museums appear to have been subjected to some degree of thermal metamorphism in their parent meteorite planet(s). Metamorphism changes rock textures and mineral compositions.

147

FIG. 1. One particular size fraction (−10 + 20 sieve meshes) of chondrules separated from the chondrite Bjurböle, with millimeter scale. (Reproduced from *Nature* **194**, 127.)

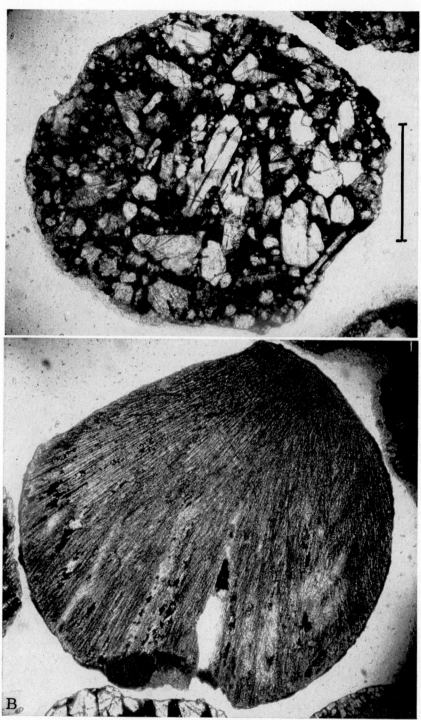

Fig. 2. Thin-sections of two chondrules separated from Bjurböle, viewed by transmitted light. Scale bar, 0.5 mm. (a) Porphyritic olivine chondrule. (b) Radiating fibrous orthopyroxene chondrule. (Reproduced from "The Solar System," Vol. IV, Chapter 12. Univ. of Chicago Press, Chicago, 1962.)

However, some chondrites seem to have been less affected by metamorphism than others. Renazzo (Fig. 4), for example, cannot have been heated extensively, because it contains unstable mineral assemblages which would not survive heating (Wood, 1962).

Renazzo consists of chondrules embedded in an ultrafine-grained, Fe_3O_4-bearing matrix (Fig. 5). The chondrules contain abundant metallic iron, but their silicate minerals are *devoid of ferrous iron*, although these minerals (olivine, pyroxene) accept ferrous iron in their lattices. Terrestrial and metamorphosed meteoritic olivines and pyroxenes do contain ferrous iron.

The complete absence of oxidized iron in Renazzo's chondrules is evidence of formation in a reducing chemical environment, such as a hydrogen-rich atmosphere. This suggests that chondrules might be the condensation products from cooling solar gases, with at least part of the condensation taking place in the liquid field of magnesium silicates. (It is usually assumed that the nonvolatile elements condensed directly from vapor to solid particles during the formation of the solar system.) Suess (1949) proposed that chondrules are liquid droplets that condensed in cooling protoplanets; I later suggested liquid condensation in the preplanetary solar nebula (Wood, 1958).

Suess (in this volume) has outlined the pressure-temperature conditions under which silicate and iron droplets are stable in an atmosphere of solar composition. These are $T > 1800°K$, $P > \sim100$ atm, based on thermochemical calculations. This is an embarrassingly high pressure to expect in the preplanetary nebula. If chondrules are indeed primary liquid condensations, then either (a) or (b), below, would be true.

(a) Some fractionating process acted to change the ratio (nonvolatile elements)/H_2 in the system. As this ratio increases, the minimum pressure of liquid stability decreases by the same factor. However, a concentration factor of $\sim10^4$ would be required to make liquids stable in the nebula at the radius of the asteroid belt, according to the model of Cameron (1962).

(b) Droplet condensation took place close to the sun ($r < \sim0.1$ a.u.), where nebular pressures were high. In this case, the hardened chondrules must have been transported outward in the nebula, some as far as the asteroid belt, before they accreted into larger bodies. Hoyle's (1960) model envisages condensation near the sun and subsequent outward transport.

Even if some liquid condensation did take place in the nebula, much nebular gas must have cooled at pressures too low for liquid stability, probably yielding ultrafine dust as condensate. Perhaps the fine matrix in Renazzo (Fig. 5) was once dispersed colloidal matter. Although solar gas reduces iron at high temperature, it will oxidize iron to Fe_3O_4 at $T <$

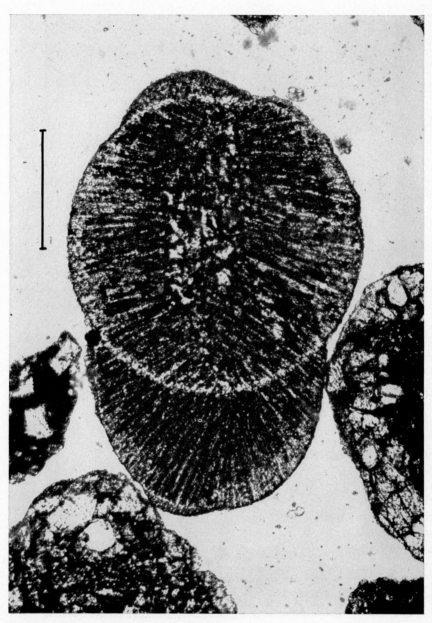

Fig. 3. Thin-section of two orthopyroxene chondrules from Bjurböle. These appear to have coalesced while one was still plastic. Scale bar, 0.2 mm. (Reproduced from Wood, 1962.)

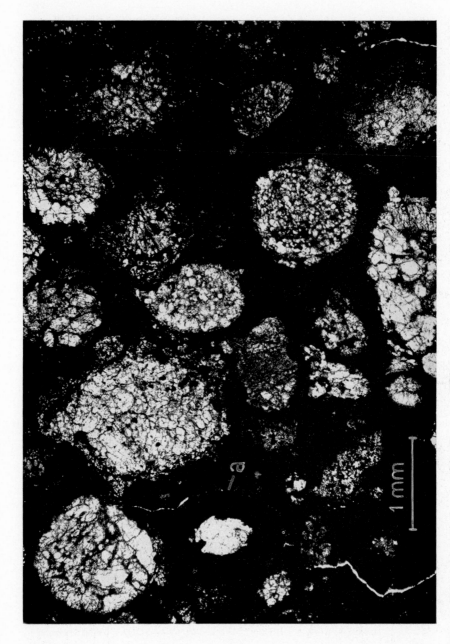

FIG. 4. Thin-section of the chondrite Renazzo. White areas, transparent silicate chondrules. Black, mostly fine-grained opaque matrix. a, ovoid chondrule with silicate core and metallic iron shell. (Reproduced from "The Solar System," Vol. IV, Chapter 12. Univ. of Chicago Press, Chicago, 1962.)

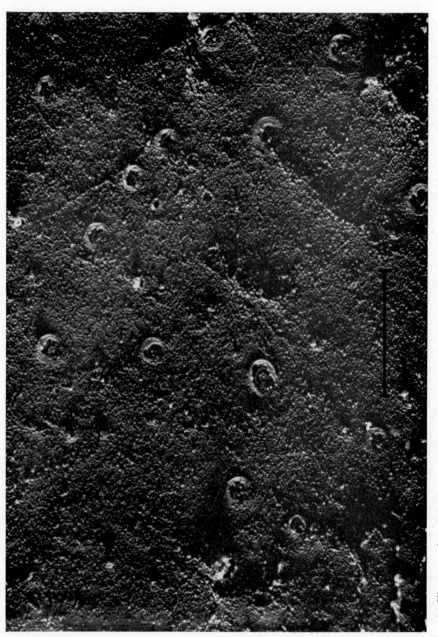

Fig. 5. Electron microscope photograph of polished surface on opaque matrix material in Renazzo. Scale bar, 1 μ. Note extremely fine grain size. Nature of the crater-like structures is not known. (Reproduced from Wood, 1962.)

~370°K. If the nebular mixture of gas and solid particles cooled fairly rapidly, the coarse iron grains embedded in chondrules would have been shielded from oxidation, while dispersed colloidal iron particles were oxidized, resulting in the curious juxtaposition of oxidation state of iron we observe in Renazzo. Subsequent thermal metamorphism of Renazzo would diffuse ferrous iron from the matrix into the chondrule silicates, yielding the equilibrium ferrous iron-bearing olivines and pyroxenes we find in most chondrites.

REFERENCES

Urey, H. C. (1952) "The Planets," p. 199. Yale Univ. Press, New Haven, Connecticut.

Wood, J. A. (1958) *Smithsonian Astrophys. Obs. Tech. Rept. No.* **10**.

Wood, J. A. (1962) *Geochim. et Cosmochim. Acta* **26**, 739.

Cameron, A. G. W. (1962) *Icarus* **1**, 13.

Hoyle, F. (1960) *Quart. J. Roy. Astron. Soc.* **1**, 28

Suess, H. E. (1949) *Z. Elektrochem.* **53**, 237.

The Interiors of the Planets

G. J. F. MacDONALD

Institute of Geophysics and Planetary Physics, University of California, Los Angeles, California

A study of the interiors of the planets can probably best be approached by considering the differences in the mean densities among them. Mercury is believed to have a density of about 5.6; Venus, 4.9; Earth, 5.52; Moon, 3.32; and Mars, 5.5. All of these are uncertain values.

The question is: how are these differences in densities brought about? They can either result from different behavior of material under different physical conditions, or they can represent real chemical differences. Let's explore chemical differences; specifically, variations in those elements that determine mass (oxygen, magnesium, silicon, and iron), and those that determine long-term thermal balance (potassium, uranium, and thorium).

Is it possible to say something from the planetary properties, such as we know them, about the possible variation of these elements? It might be useful to begin with the planet about which we know the most, the Earth, and briefly summarize the relevant geophysical information that provides a control for the construction of models for the other planets.

What we know about the interior of the earth comes almost entirely from seismology. Some depth characteristics of the Gutenberg Earth model are shown in Fig. 1.

The four features to note in this model are as follows. First, the wave velocity actually decreases between about 30 and 200 km. This feature plus the details of the rest of the curve have been established rather recently as a result of the Earth's free oscillation. The second feature is a rather rapid rise in elastic velocities between 200 and 900 km, and then a less rapid rise. Then there is the break separating the core of the earth from the mantle, the core being identified by the fact that shear waves, both short-period and long-period shear waves, are not transmitted in this

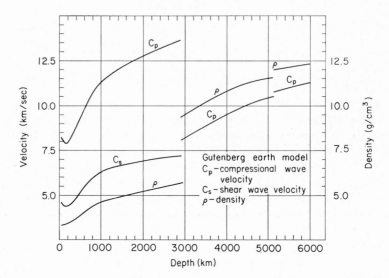

FIG. 1. Some depth characteristics of the Gutenberg Earth model.

region. The discontinuity in elastic wave velocity is fairly well determined. Finally, there is an inner break, a rather small inner core, the nature of which is extremely uncertain.

Several points here are important. First, the dip in velocity almost certainly is due to the combined effects of temperature and pressure. When the temperature is raised a silicate structure is opened up, and becomes more compressible, less rigid. An increase in temperature thus tends to lower the elastic wave velocities. The effect of pressure is just the opposite. In this region it would appear that temperature is winning out over pressure and that there is no necessity for assuming these compositional differences.

The next inner region presents a problem. A possible reason for the anomalously large increase in elastic wave velocity may be an actual change in the physical structure of the material. The kinds of transformation that have been considered include the Fosteroid form of olivine, in which the olivine goes into a spinel-type structure. The principal difference in this structure is that the oxygens attain a somewhat closer packing in this higher density form. The estimated volume change for such a transition is on the order of 0.1. This assumption is uncertain because this form has not as yet been synthesized in the laboratory. Attempts have been made to approach it by using germanium. Substituting the germanium analogue for silicon, the process goes at somewhat lower pressures.

A further point should be emphasized. This transition maintains the silicon in four-coordination; that is, the silicon remains in a tetrahedral arrangement surrounded by oxygens. The structure still has some openness about it because of the preference for the silica to assume this four coordination.

The conditions under which this transition takes place are uncertain. Again they depend on extrapolation of the germanium analogues and germanium silica solid solutions. A later graph will show the approximate temperature-pressure conditions under which this takes place.

A second transition, which I suspect is far more important, is one in which the olivine goes into the oxide where the silica is now in the form of a six-coordinated silicon. It is a new compound, synthesized by Stishov and Popova in Russia, and since then has been found observationally in the Canyon Diablo crater by Chao and his co-workers.

The point here is that unlike the transition in which the silicon remains in four-coordination, leading to a certain openness in the structure, all the oxygens are in close packing.

There is very little give in the geometrical arrangement of the oxygens. It may be that the only further transitions are those in which one actually begins to shift the electron energy levels, and obtains pressure ionization by moving the electrons up into the conducting bands.

The change in volume in this reaction is 0.2, about 20% decrease in volume. The density of quartz is 2.62; the density of the high pressure form of SiO_2 is 4.32. Thus this is a major adjustment in volume.

One suggestion is that the material in the region of rapid rise in wave velocity is undergoing a phase transition from the lower density forms to higher density forms. Perhaps both of these transitions take place, the spinel transition coming into four-coordination; then the breakdown into the oxides.

Figure 2 gives another picture of the distribution within the earth of the density, pressure, and gravitational acceleration. The latter is fairly constant up to the core boundary. The maximum pressure that is reached is about 3.6 megabars.

Figure 3 shows an experimentally determined transition curve between two forms of the SiO_2; quartz with a 2.6 density and coesite with a 3.0 density. There is also a calculated curve for the transition between the coesite and the stishovite, using the Russian results where account is taken of their experimental apparatus.

In this case the $P\Delta V$ term in the equilibrium relations swamps out virtually everything else. High pressure (P) times the very large change of volume (V) is the major energy adjustment that is involved. The general position of the curve can be fairly well established.

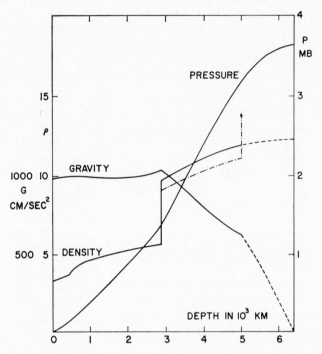

FIG. 2. Density, pressure, and acceleration within the Earth (after Bullen).

Figure 4 shows the $P\Delta V$ term in relation to the elastic wave velocities. This is the ratio of the incompressibility to the density.

Note the region in which phase changes probably are occurring in the olivine-spinel. Perhaps there is also a change of the olivine to the higher pressure forms or the spinel form to the higher density oxide stishovite forms.

The important point is that this is a transition that takes place at pressures of 100,000 atm. These are pressures that are reached in at least two of the planets—Mars and Venus—and therefore may be important in determining the internal structure.

The nature of the third boundary, or the nature of the discontinuity at the core-mantle boundary, is still uncertain. The bulk of the evidence points to a major compositional change. The classical interpretation is that one goes from a silicate-like material, high pressure form, to a metal, largely iron-nickel. This sort of thinking, of course, is heavily influenced by the nature of meteorites.

However, because of the uncertainty in the density variation, there actually may be a good deal less change compositionally. And because

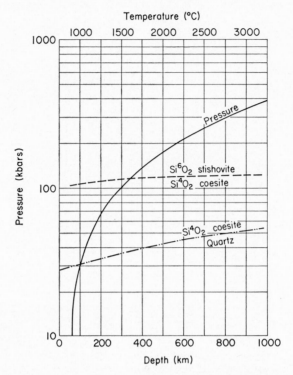

Fig. 3. Experimentally determined transition curve between two forms of SiO² —quartz and coesite; also a calculated curve for the transition between coesite and stishovite.

of the lack of knowledge of what compounds do at pressures of 1.2 megabars, there is still some possibility that this also may represent a phase change, though I think this is less likely than a compositional change.

As far as the actual variation of density is concerned in constructing other planets, one should take into account the phase changes in the pressure range near 10^5 atm. The change of volume will be from 10% to 20%. There also may be an additional phase change at the higher pressure of about 10^6 atm. This would be important only in the case of Venus.

The second set of data that is of considerable interest in constructing planetary models is derived from the satellite observations of the figure of the Earth. The reason for this is that the figure obtained from satellite data is not what one would expect for an equilibrium body. There are deviations that are not understood. We can make our hypotheses about them, but they do indicate the sort of deviations one would expect for other planets.

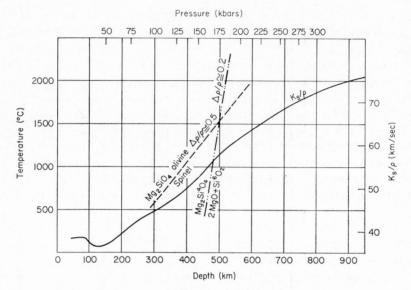

Fig. 4. The $P\Delta V$ term in relation to the elastic wave velocities.

For Mars, for example, there is a good measure of the ratio of the moment of inertia about the axis of rotation to the least moment, over the mass times the radius squared. This is an observed quantity. One may wish to construct a hydrostatic model of Mars. One would then want a measure of the possible deviations of the hydrostatic model from the model actually observed.

So it is of interest to look at the order of magnitude of these deviations of the Earth's density field from that of an equilibrium body. There are many ways of listing them. Perhaps the best way is in terms of types of stresses represented by this nonequilibrium distribution of mass. This distribution will lead to certain stress differences within the body. We can make an estimate of what maximum stress differences are obtained.

For the Earth, the sort of maximum stress differences that you must have to support the second harmonic are about 20 to 30 atm. The third harmonic requires somewhat less, about 10 atm, and higher harmonics about the same.

The Earth is out of equilibrium by a certain amount. One measure of this amount is the maximum stress differences to which these inequalities of mass will lead.

Various interpretations can be given to these stress differences. The one that I would favor at present is that the Earth as a whole is an elastic body with a certain amount of strength; it can support stress differences of a considerable order of magnitude. If the stress differences become appreciably larger, fracturing or plasticity of some sort tend to relieve these stress differences.

A further interpretation could be given to the second harmonic. This is the harmonic that indicates that the earth is a little too fat, i.e., that the actual bulge of the Earth is about 1.5% larger than it should be for an Earth rotating at its present angular velocity. The interpretation that Walter Munk and I gave is that this merely represents the result of the circular distortion of the Earth, and that the present-day figure is the figure that the Earth would have had a certain time ago, the time being dependent on the rate at which the Earth is being decelerated. If one translates this into a time constant, a relaxation time, it is about 10^7 or 10^8 years. This is not a unique interpretation.

An alternative model that one could construct is one in which stress differences are built up until they are relieved and there is *no* continuous relaxation of the stresses.

The important point is that these deviations from the equilibrium figure are observed on the earth and perhaps indicate the magnitude of the stress differences that one might expect on other planets, appropriately scaled for size and mass.

The third body of information relates to three elements as far as the Earth is concerned. Measurements have been made of the rate at which heat is flowing from the surface, and the temperature gradient and thermal conductivity have been determined at about a hundred points on the Earth's surface, land and ocean. The range of these measurements is large. However, in any given area, with two exceptions—Japan and the Easter Island areas—the mean is very close to a mean flux of about 50 ergs/cm²/sec. Thus the rate at which heat is apparently flowing from the earth is about 50 ergs/cm²/sec.

The solar constant is 2×10^5 larger.

So the heat flux exercises absolutely no control on the near surface temperature.

This number, plus the numbers on the abundance of the elements in chondritic meteorites, have led to models of the earth. A coincidence of two sets of numbers has played a very important role in the construction of models of the Earth. Chondritic meteorites on the average have a potassium content of 8×10^{-4} gm/gm; the uranium content, 1.1×10^{-8} gm/gm; thorium, about four times as large, 4×10^{-8} gm/gm.

If we take a chrondritic Earth—that is, an Earth having these radioactive elements with these abundances—and if all the heat produced is flowing from the surface, the value is 59 ergs/cm²/sec (Table I). (A

TABLE I

HEAT PRODUCTION IN A CHONDRITIC EARTH

	Heat production (ergs/sec)	"Equilibrium" surface heat flow (ergs/cm²/sec)
Chondritic Earth (present)	3.01×10^{20}	59.0
Chondritic Earth (4.5×10^9 years ago)	24.30×10^{20}	476
Chondritic Mantle (present)	2.04×10^{20}	40.2
Chondritic Mantle (4.5×10^9 years ago)	16.50×10^{20}	324

steady-state heat flow is assumed.) This is to be compared with the same kind of heat flow, 4.5×10^9 years ago of 476 ergs/cm²/sec. If only the mantle were chrondritic, this figure would be divided by two-thirds. These are equivalent surface heat flows if the heat produced by radio-activity reached the surface instantaneously.

The coincidence of these two numbers has suggested to several people that this could be a representative model for the composition of the Earth. The difficulty centers around the contribution of the heat produced in the past due to the higher rate of heat production, and also any contributions that might have arisen from the fact that the Earth had some initial temperature. These are the two things that would tend to raise these figures.

On the basis of these values, one can construct models to show the temperature distribution within the Earth. These probably do nothing more than indicate the relative play between such factors as where you put the heat sources, what the initial temperature might do, how you start the calculations, and so on. It suggests that if you put too much of the radioactivity very deep within the Earth, then the temperature will rise above the melting point and one would expect that some fraction of the earth today would be molten or nearly molten. This is the basis of the argument that there has been some separation within the Earth. It is almost certain that a good deal of potassium has gotten to the surface. My assumption is that the heat is transferred by the solid material as a gray body. There is lattice conduction and there is radiative transfer.

One might ask: is not much of the heat transferred by convection—that is, actual mass motion within the mantle? This is an extremely difficult point to discuss because we are dealing with a body that is elastic for deformations of 14 months, probably longer. The nature of convection is most uncertain. Undoubtedly there is convection in the sense that there is local melting and the heat is transported actually by the molten material. This is convection, but of an irregular kind. I doubt very seriously that there would be nice Benard-like cells rolling away in the mantle. One can probably assume that even if the material did behave like a viscous fluid, the range of Rayleigh numbers over which one would get this nice regular pattern is very small. The total range of Rayleigh numbers, the theory of convection in a stratified fluid, in which there is density stratification, has not been looked at. It is perhaps one of the two key problems in geophysics today.

What amount of energy is needed to melt the mantle? The mass of the earth is 6×10^{27} gm. Two-thirds of that is in the mantle, 4×10^{27} gm. The heat of melting in a multi-component solution is probably on the order of 50 to 100 cal/gm. Translating this to ergs, it is 4×10^7 ergs/gm, or a total for the Earth of some 2×10^{35} ergs.

The convection difficulty is a serious one. I don't know how to answer the geologists who continually point out that the ocean floor is being swept off once every ten million years and sediments are being poured underneath. One can only say that the logical interpretation of these quantities is based entirely on the strength of the material supporting stress differences. If one has mass motions, one can construct models in which these inequalities are supported by the actual viscous stresses. These motions will have an effect on the moment of inertia that would show up in the Chandler wobble, and they don't.

With this very brief and inadequate outline of the important elements of geophysics, we can now ask what sort of model one can construct of the moon. Almost all inferences regarding the internal constitution of the moon follow from data on its orbital and rotational motion. The moon's motion leads to the mean density and also leads to an estimate, somewhat inadequate, of the gravitational figure.

A further possible limitation to the thermal constitution of the moon comes from a comparison of the radio emission temperature of the lunar surface at several wavelengths. The high frequency emission presumably is from the near surface; the low frequency emission is from somewhat deeper depths. If there is a consistent difference in temperature between these two, then this can lead to an estimate of heat flow. The data on this are extremely poor, but worth mentioning.

The density is 3.34, significantly less than the density of chondritic materials. Urey has pointed this out and has suggested a number of other chemical models for the moon that involve the addition of water, carbon compounds of various sorts. All are possibilities.

It is striking that the density that one would calculate for the solar abundances would also be less than the chondritic abundances. Urey notes that if one takes Aller's solar atmosphere abundances and reconstructs a rock out of them, it will have a density of 3.2 or 3.3.

It also should be noted that the moon's density is not too far from that of two rocks that many believe might make up the upper parts of the Earth's mantle. These are common magnesium–iron silicates. Both have densities that are very close to 3.3–3.2. The gravitational figure of the moon provides perhaps the best limits.

From the physical liberations of the moon we can deduce differences in its principal moments of inertia.

It turns out that the moon has a bulge much too big for its present rate of rotation. It also has a protrusion towards and away from the earth that is much too large for the present tidal attraction.

Thus the moon's figure reveals that large inequalities in the figure are supported today. In terms of stress differences, they are of the same order as stress differences supported within the earth; that is, 20 bars.

Furthermore, there is nothing in the quantities derived from the moon's motion that is inconsistent with the idea that the moon is homogeneous. But the values are not very good.

What can be done about this? One thing would be to consider what would be the thermal structure of the moon, assuming chondritic radio-activity and that the moon is more or less homogeneous.

Figure 5 gives an example of a calculation in which one assumes that the moon was at zero degrees 4.5×10^9 years ago.

The chondritic radioactivity is assumed to be distributed uniformly. One calculates the present distribution of temperature within the moon. Figure 5 shows the curve that is obtained. Also shown are experimentally-determined melting curves. The outside curve is simply an upper limit for the melting of silicates. The true melting temperature is undoubtedly lower.

The conclusion is that it is impossible to have a moon with this radio-activity uniformly distributed and yet have a moon that does not melt. One can juggle the figures however he wishes, and he still either comes extremely close to or exceeds the melting temperature by a large amount.

There is a discrepancy between the strength indicated by the moments of inertia and the assumption of uniform radioactivity. Let us examine the relaxation of one of these conditions.

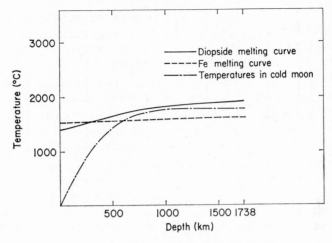

Fig. 5. See text.

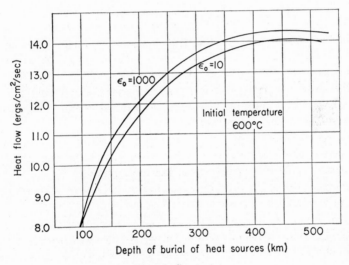

Fig. 6. See text.

Figure 6 shows a different kind of plot. Here one starts out with an initial temperature of 600°C. The radioactivity is concentrated within the indicated distance from the surface. The maximum temperature is reached within the moon at a depth of 400 km. The two curves represent different assumptions about the opacity. By assuming that the moon has this composition, one can get away from this difficulty of having simultaneously a molten moon and a strong moon.

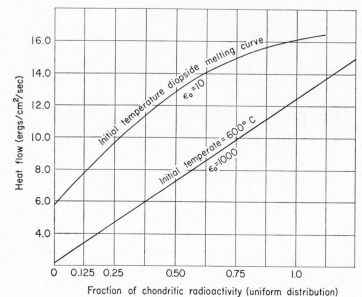

FIG. 7. See text.

Figure 7 indicates the alternative, the same sort of calculation. But here one considers different fractions of chondritic radioactivity, maintaining the same ratios among the various elements. The point is that if one starts considering fractions, one has to go down to about a third of the chondritic radioactivity, perhaps a fifth, to keep the moon from melting. Otherwise, provided that the radioactivity elements are uniformly distributed, the moon will melt.

Thus the alternatives are to push the radioactivity near the surface, or to remove it. The difficulty with the hypothesis of differentiation is in determining which mechanism will provide a separation, so that one can push these elements towards the surface without actually going through a molten phase.

There is one further line of evidence on the moon that I think is important; that is, the rate at which the moon is moving away from the Earth. The names associated with this problem are Darwin, Jeffries, and Taylor.

The tidal interaction between the Earth and the moon dissipates energy. At the same time angular momentum is transferred from the rotation of the Earth to the moon, so that as the Earth slows down the moon accelerates.

The reanalysis of the data on the secular acceleration of the moon has indicated that previous estimates of this rate of energy dissipation were low by about a factor of 3. Furthermore, it is clear that this dissipation does not take place in shallow ocean. Recently measurements of the tides in the Bering Sea indicate that they don't run at anywhere near the 2 knots required to dissipate the energy in the sea, nor do they run at the required velocity over any shallow sea. The rate at which energy is being dissipated within the sea is actually a small fraction of the total.

A number of measurements are being made in both this country and Russia of the lag in phase of the bodily tide in the solid earth. This tide is about a meter in height, usually measurable in terms of its effects on the acceleration of a long-period pendulum. The phase lags run about one to two degrees in mid-continent ocean, far away from effects of loading of the ocean.

This suggests, then, that the dissipation is actually taking place in the body of the Earth, not in the sea. And if it is taking place within the body of the Earth, then the time constants associated with changing the dissipation must be very long. If the dissipation were in the sea, one could always change sea level, change the height of land in the sea, and change the amount of shallow seas so that any extrapolation back in time would be somewhat dubious because of the changing sink for the energy.

If it is taking place within the body of the Earth, the thermal time constants are very long and the pressure remains the same. There is no reason to expect that there would be changes of appreciable magnitude in the dissipation and elastic properties of the Earth.

If this is so, then taking the present rate at which the moon is swinging out and integrating back in time, we arrive at a point about 5×10^8 years ago that the moon was much too near to the Earth, within the Roche limit.

This, then, raises the question, how old is the Earth-moon system? Is it possible that the Earth-moon system is a rather recent affair? Could the moon have been captured, let's say, in the last few hundred million years?

There are a number of points that one could raise. Perhaps it would be worthwhile to look into the hypothesis of the moon being captured late in the history of the earth.

Let us now consider Mars, because there we again have information on the extent of the equatorial bulge. This is derived from the study of the motion of the satellites Phobus and Deimos.

If one assumes that Mars is in hydrostatic equilibrium, one could then obtain flattening. But we won't do that. Rather, we will calculate models of the amount of flattening by determining the distribution of density within Mars. That, taking into account its present angular velocity, will give us the correct mass for Mars.

The three parameters that we might have are: (1) the surface density; (2) a chemical inhomogeneity; and (3) the boundary where that chemical inhomogeneity is located. In addition, there are two more free parameters: the pressure at which the phase transition takes place, and the density change at that transition. By chemical inhomogeneity we mean the proportion of iron in the model, and the position of the boundary indicates how big the core may be.

The uncertainty in the radius of the solid body of Mars results in a further complication. Studies indicate that the radius of Mars has a range of values with a large probable error. The values used in my model are 3389 km, and I have also made some calculations with Rabe's old values.

The flattening as obtained from the observed value of the second harmonic of the figure is 520×10^{-5}. This would imply stress differences on the order of 10 bars.

The core radius is plotted in Fig. 8. The core is taken to have the properties of the Earth's core, using the law of corresponding states as far as density is concerned. With compressibility again modeled on the Earth's compressibility, the surface density is plotted as a function of the flattening and the radius of the core. Taking the radius of a solid body as 3345 km which is about 30 km larger than usually assumed, the surface density would be 3.9 if the body were hydrostatic. There would be no core to speak of.

If one moves down to 500×10^{-5}, which is about the limit indicated by the strength of the earth, the surface density would go down to 3.8. If one goes to 470, surface density is around 3.6. This is using the most favorable case for the radius.

Similar results are obtained if we assume a smaller radius. The point is, of course, that the mass and dynamical figure of Mars are consistent only with the material that is almost homogeneous. There may be a phase change involved; there is no core.

I can quickly give you the effect of the phase transitions. Changing the constants on the phase transition only changes the density by 0.05. It goes from 3.6 to 3.55. There is no big play there and one is left with a homogeneous body. When this happens there is melting, and there should be a core.

The dynamical orbital constants suggest that Mars must be homogeneous or nearly homogeneous, like chondrites. The density is a bit too low, but some chondrites have such densities. If a certain amount of radioactivity is introduced, the core melts. So the body can't be homogeneous.

One must conclude that these may not be representative for Mars, and that the radioactivity in Mars is less than that for chondrites.

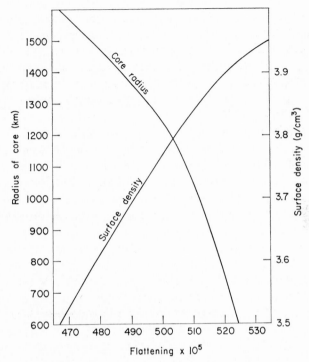

FIG. 8. Surface density and core radius for Mars; radius = 3345 km.

There is one additional point, dealing with the secular acceleration of Phobus.

The secular acceleration has been determined by Sharpless, and it can be explained entirely in terms of solid tides with a phase lag of about a degree or a degree and a half, whereas the phase lag of the earth is about two degrees.

This suggestion that the inelastic properties of Mars are not different from those of the earth indicates that this is a fairly solid body. If it were a fluid, or a mixture of molten silicates and other material, the rate at which the energy dissipates would go up.

Problems Requiring Solution

THOMAS GOLD

Cornell University, Ithaca, New York

The most serious problems in the attempt to establish a basic line of evolution of the solar system appear to center around three points. These are:

(1) The method of agglomeration of solid pieces. How do they manage to stick together, especially over a certain range of size?

(2) The magnetohydrodynamics that are involved in transferring angular momentum as far out as necessary by the magnetic field anchored in a body as small as the sun.

(3) The problem of escape from the sun of all the extra hydrogen that is believed to be present in the region of the outer planets.

The method of agglomeration of solids has been discussed, and it has been suggested that some ices must be present to make the surfaces adhere. But isn't it possible that gravitational instabilities could take a large volume of finely distributed dust and make it all come together eventually? I don't know, but it would seem that there should have been some discussion on that point.

There is also the possibility that the sticking was started by magnetic particles—iron particles—which would adhere perfectly well, up to a small size. In order for gravitational forces eventually to set in, the nucleation would have to be built up from iron lumps; there is nothing wrong with that, because silicates would be added only when the object is gravitationally active.

Then, too, one must consider the possibility of an agglomeration bridging the difficult gap between objects that are centimeters or a meter in size, and those that are gravitationally active (a kilometer or more in size). This gap is the most difficult to bridge, because as yet gravitation is not in the picture.

It is possible that a nucleation of the condensation process bridges the gap by having a lump of a few kilometers—which very reasonably may be a comet—eventually become the nucleus for a planet. If one considers that a large volume of dust particles or small lumps—or a mixture of the two—are orbiting in the inner parts of the solar system, then it is reasonable to assume that occasionally large chunks would come through and sweep up a certain amount of the material. Their orbits would be attenuated by that and contracted. The object created thus acquires the small pieces and eventually grows by gravitation.

Let us now turn for a moment to the magnetic winding problem. Does the winding up of the lines of force due to the differential rotation occur all the way out so that any such configuration will be wound up very tightly? Or are there dissipative processes in the gas which would cut out the extremely sheared field?

I suppose that one tends to think a little too much of a perfect configuration, because the moment that one thinks of fields that possess a variation in longitude intrinsically at the sun, then such a wound-up field will result in the juxtaposition of opposing lines of force. Then, there will be some lines that have one sense, and nearby there will be a layer changing over to the opposite sense. Such a situation, of course, will attenuate very quickly.

As we now understand it, the main reason for dissipation of magnetic fields of tenuous gases is indeed the juxtaposition of opposing lines of force inadequately separated by gas pressure.

Perhaps a picture which would be a little more realistic, because of the kind of magnetic behavior of the sun, would be in terms of individual magnetic clouds strung through the pre-existing outer material, and the angular momentum transported out because individual tongues have pushed their way through all this. And the thing is stitched together with lines of force that go backwards and forwards. Then there would be a constant process of dissipation and at the same time constant replenishment of strung-out fields from any kind of solar activity.

Perhaps that is the way it does happen, and perhaps it is in that way very dependent on the activity on the surface of the sun at the time.

I am always very keen on trying. I try to see whether an explanation can be found in terms which would indicate that a little of that process is happening now. Then we can watch the process more carefully and perhaps learn more from it. So just from the hopeful point of view, when we better understand what is happening on the sun now, we will perhaps be able to produce a clearer picture of what happened in the past. If it was a process that is very different from anything that is going on now, then we are in a much poorer position to find out.

Then there is the question of the escape of the hydrogen from the CNO on the outer parts of the solar system. I am aware of the difficulty of a diffusive separation in the time scale in the following sense: I remember the discussion, which in many respects is very wide of the mark of Alfven's story of the origin of the solar system. But it had one point of interest; namely, that to drag the different components of the gas by diffusive separation through each other, even when one constituent has its full gravitational weight and the other none, still takes several times 10^9 years. And that, it seems to me, can be shown to be the biggest force that one can possibly have between the two components that are to be separated.

From that point of view, none of the dynamics that one could have out there could apply as large a force as that, and that would be the upper limit. It seems clear that if it is to be done in a shorter time schedule, one must condense the CNO into lumps and then dispose of the remainder, rather than try to separate the CNO from the hydrogen in the gaseous phase.

So whatever the details were of the discussion about how to blow off hydrogen at the edge of the solar system, it seems to me an improbable process. The elements cannot be sorted out well enough, even with the biggest force available. There is no hardship about doing it the other way. The main discussion still stands.

To get rid of the hydrogen out there, just with the radiant solar flux as Hoyle has discussed, one needs to strain one's self to say the least.

A much smaller amount of energy would indeed suffice to blow off that material if it were supplied in bursts or in a patchy way.

If a little energy is concentrated in a small amount of material at one time, then that can be entirely removed. Once the matter is separated in pieces, it won't blow off no matter what is done.

Then some energy can be concentrated into a bit of the remaining gas and the whole of that gas can be removed. The energy requirements come out to be much less, because otherwise most of the energy goes through that material as radiant flux, and is not being used. A great quantity of radiant flux is required to get those 3 km per second that the atoms need to be released.

If the energy were to be concentrated, much less would be required, and therefore it would seem desirable to suggest some other solar activity method of getting rid of the gas. An occasional outburst from the sun would be much more effective in blowing off material out there if the temperature of that gas were changed substantially.

Particle fluxes out there can perhaps do that. It seems also not absolutely sure that the energy for the last of this material actually does come from the sun. It also would be conceivable to consider the energy coming from the outside as a consequence of the wind in which the solar system will find itself. If one supposes 15 km per second, or so, and quite reasonable densities, enough energy can be pumped into the region out there to remove gas, but again it would not do if it were put in uniformly.

But it could be put in in some concentrated way. For example, with the dynamics of an accretion system, where a jet of outside gas might be squirted to punch a hole through a rather narrow region at a time, and therefore remove a bit at a time. This again is much more economical than to heat the whole lot. In heating the entire lot, most of the energy is lost in other ways than by evaporation so that concentrated heating from outside is also a possibility.

These seem to me the points that require the most study. Of course, I am quite naive about the nuclear evidence, so I will not comment on that. I do not wish it to be thought that I don't consider that evidence to be important; such rapid progress is being made with the evidence that comes from nuclear physics investigations and from chemistry that that is not a subject at which one has to point one's finger at the moment; however, these three topics that I mentioned seem to me to really need further attention to make clear the main outline of the process.

SUBJECT INDEX